KUDZU

The Vine to Love or Hate

KUDZU

The Vine to Love or Hate

Diane Hoots
and
Juanitta Baldwin

Suntop Press
Kodak, Tennessee 37764
Virginia Beach, Virginia 23462

 This is a book about kudzu - pueraria lobata/thunbergiana. Although the authors have researched all sources to produce complete and accurate data, they assume no responsibility for errors, inaccuracies, omissions, or any inconsistency herein because this book is not intended to supplace specialized advice in any specific situation. Anything that may be interpreted as a slight is unintentional.

Printed and bound in the United States of America
First Printing 1996
10 9 8 7 6 5 4 3 2 1

ISBN - 1-880308-12-6

Library of Congress Cataloging-in-Publication Data

Hoots, Diane,
Kudzu, the vine to love or hate / Diane Hoots and Juanitta Baldwin.
p. cm.
ISBN 1-880308-12-6 (pbk. : alk. paper)
1. Kudzu--Southern States. 2. Kudzu--Control--Southern States.
I. Baldwin, Juanitta, . II. Title.
SB615.K83H66 1996
363.7'8--dc20 96-23838
CIP

Dedication

~~~~~

My work in this book is dedicated to:

Janie Sue Yearwood
May 30, 1937 - August 27, 1995

anie loved life and kudzu; I loved her kindred spirit.

Diane Hoots

~~~~~~

My work in this book is dedicated,

with love, to my sister,

Mary Jane Stallcup Joyner,

for appreciation for the joy we share -

from blackberries- through pep and oatmeal -

- to kudzu - to whatever!

Juanitta Baldwin

We wish each reader of this book a state of tranquility throughout your life.

About this Book
Kudzu The Vine to Love or Hate

We have three major topics in this book:

- how kudzu came to be such a presence in the Southeast and the urgent need to contain it,
- things innovative people are now doing with kudzu, and
- the need for a capitalist to create something that uses *lots* of kudzu and turn this maligned vine into a valuable asset.

Our purpose is to rouse and share interest in kudzu and suggest its scope rather than attempt to exhaust it. Readers may find contradictions in what persons working with kudzu say and do. That is the way it is in the world of kudzu. Our goal was to report it just the way it is.

We have a comprehensive data base on kudzu. If you have information, an experience or story about kudzu you would like to share, please check the information on our Kudzu Data Base in Appendix B of this book. Perhaps we can publish it in our next book.

We do anticipate writing another book because we had more information than we could put in this one. Writing this book was a unique, unforgettable experience as well as great fun. The fun part came from contacts with many very talented, interesting, and helpful persons. To each we extend our sincere appreciation.

~~~~~~~~~~

This book is available at Diane Hoots' classes, lectures and seminars on kudzu, and at craft shows.

It may be purchased through any bookstore serviced by Baker & Taylor, the book wholesalers, or from V. Elizabeth Waddell, Suntop Press Representative, P. O. Box 98, Kodak, Tennessee 37764.
~~~~~~~~~~

STATE OF GEORGIA

OFFICE OF THE GOVERNOR

ATLANTA 30334-0900

Zell Miller
GOVERNOR

January 8, 1995

Ms. Diane Hoots
Krazy Kudzu Products, Ltd.
Post Office Box 8584
Warner Robins, Georgia 31095-8584

Dear Diane:

Thank you so much for the autographed copy of 101 Uses of Kudzu. Having lived with this vine all my life, I look back and think of all the things I could have used it for if I had only had your book. It is interesting and will be a great addition to the Governor's Mansion library. We have a section on Georgia authors and your book will be placed among the other wonderful publications we have collected.

Shirley and I received a beautiful Kudzu basket for Christmas, and we have had so many of the Mansion visitors comment on the originality of the material. Folks cannot believe it is woven from Kudzu vines. I find it hard to believe myself.

We hope you have a successful and happy new year.

With warmest personal regards, I remain

Sincerely,

Zell Miller

ZM/mg

About the Authors

Diane Hoots is a certified science teacher. Through study and hands-on experience since 1985, she has become an expert on kudzu and is in much demand as a speaker and teacher of art and craft classes. Her audiences include school classes from grammar school through college credit courses, workshops for attendees at state fairs, kudzu festivals, museums and special interest groups.

Diane owns Krazy Kudzu Products, LTD. in Warner Robins, Georgia, which markets arts, crafts and food products made from kudzu, and books about kudzu. She markets by direct sales, television, and in stores throughout the Southeastern United States.

~~~~~~~~~~~~

Juanitta Baldwin became fascinated with kudzu while studying herbs and turned it into an avocation. She owns Kudzu Gold®, a firm specializing in creating designs for using kudzu in arts and crafts, and creating original pieces of kudzu jewelry.

Juanitta is a psychologist and writer. Among her published books are *Cast a Long Shadow, Here We Go Again!, The Callico Tree, Harvesting Happiness, and Murder in Dumplin Valley.*
~~~~~~~~~~~~

KUDZU KLASS

Language alert: Kudzu triggers a language malfunction between the letters 'K' and 'C' in many folks. You don't have to be in contact with the plant to experience this malfunction. All you have to do is think, write or say the word 'kudzu.' To your bewilderment, you may substitute 'K' for 'C' or, occasionally, 'C' for 'K' - as in these examples:

Kudzu Klass - this professor's experience
"Kudzu Kaptured my Kar...in Georgia" - on a postcard
Krazy Kudzu
Kudzu Kountry
Kudzu Kreatives
Kudzu Konnection
Kudzu Kritters
Kudzu Kabin Designs

\~~~~~~~~

\~~~~~~~~~~~~~~~~~~~~~~~~~~~~~~~~~~~

Final Word: Beware, kudzu kan korrupt language!

Table of Contents

Part I
Overview of Kudzu in the United States

Part II
Kudzu Arts and Crafts

Part III
Kudzu in Southern Culture

Part IV
Making the Best of the Kudzu Predicament

Part V
What Lies Ahead

Appendices

Part I

Overview of Kudzu in the United States

Chapter 1
What is Kudzu

Kudzu is the ***Super Vine*** in the Southeastern United States.

It leaps tall buildings in Atlanta, and elsewhere,

it stops speeding locomotives,

and captures everything in its path with incredible speed!

How Can This Be?

These feats are possible because mother nature endowed kudzu with a gargantuan anatomy and prodigious growth rate.

Kudzu has a marvelously efficient root system. Roots radiate out from the kudzu crown in all directions and drill deep into the soil for water and nutrients. Many persons have reported digging roots from 20 feet in the ground which weighed between 400 and 500 pounds.

There is no direct ratio of root size to vine size. Vines are subject to the whims of animals, humans and the weather while the roots are snug in the soil. Roots of any size are so resilient that getting rid of kudzu is a monumental task.

Cutting the vines may or may not affect the root. They have been known to lie dormant beneath the soil for up to ten years before springing to life. The only method for removing kudzu permanently is to totally dig out the roots and destroy them. Broken roots left in the soil will grow.

Eli Preston's Saga

Eli Preston has lived on a farm in northern Mississippi for ninety years. This is his story about kudzu.

My wife Ethel loved to set by the kitchen stove on cold winter days and study the seed catalogs. Sometimes she'd get so deep in her readin' she'd forgit to put wood in the stove. But I never faulted her fer readin 'cause she worked right beside me for forty-odd years.

When Ethel made out her seed order in 1929 money was tight but she ordered a kudzu vine anyway. I helped her plant it by the front steps and before the summer was over it shaded the width of our two rockers.

Ethel loved that kudzu vine. Back then we called it the front porch vine. So when the government offered farmers money to plant acres of kudzu, I jumped at it. Me and my two oldest boys planted five acres in 1934 and got paid thirty-five dollars. That was big money that turned on me.

We didn't know what to do with the stuff and it just took my farm. We soon learned we had to dig it up and burn it or the dadburned stuff would root.

Grover, my oldest boy, went off to the war and wrote me a tale he heard about a bird that comes to life from its own ashes. I wrote him back that he'd heard wrong. That was no bird, that was kudzu!

Vines

Kudzu vines hit the ground running. Runners can sprint a foot a day. Soft brown hairs serve as running suits and offer limited protection. As the vines touch the ground, they put out roots at the points on the vine from which leaves arise. These points are called nodes and when fully rooted are called crowns. This produces new plants by vegetative propagation, a form of asexual reproduction. Reproduction by seeds is on a far lesser scale because seeds are difficult to germinate. That is why kudzu is not spread by birds.

Slender, spiraling tendrils are sent out to cling and coil around any available object that will support the vine in its climb in any direction from the ground. Vines are gregarious and intertwine intricately as they wander. Kudzu can colonize and thrive in exposed bare areas where other plants are unable to survive. Vines grow between fifty and one hundred feet in a typical growing season.

Leaves

Kudzu is deciduous and during the winter vines appear dead. Leaf production during each growing season is prolific. Leaves grow in a pattern of three from each strong, relatively short stem. The stems are three to seven inches long and firmly anchored to the vine.

The leaves develop a lush, dark green color on top with a silvery underlining. At maturity, they measure up to twelve inches high and sixteen inches wide and are covered with a coat of fine hair. They are heavy and the silver can be seen only by touching them or when the wind blows.

Oblivious to normal wind, the stems and leaves remain on the vine until fall. The leaves shrivel, turn brown and fall shortly after the first killing frost. They are an effective barrier against erosion and enrich the soil.

Flowers

The casual eye sees only green leaves in a stand of kudzu but mature plants produce flowers at the end of summer. They grow upward at the axillary region between the stem and leaf and are almost always hidden beneath the dense leaf cover. The flowers are clusters of deep purple blossoms on short stalks from an elongated center stem, similar to a cluster of grapes. The blossoms have the delightful aroma of ripe grapes.

Seeds

Seed pods, somewhat similar to soybean pods, appear as the flowers are fading, and mature in the fall. Few pods contain seeds. Even mature seeds do not sprout readily. Scratching the seed's surface before planting may increase the chances of sprouting. The pods drop from the vine about the same time as the leaves.

Botanical Classification

Kudzu is a member of the leguminosae (fabaceae) family of plants, commonly called the pea family. Kudzu and the black eye pea, prized for bringing good luck to those who eat it on New Year's Day, are cousins. The black eye pea was firmly rooted in the traditions of the southeast long before kudzu arrived in the United States from Asia.

Several varieties of kudzu were brought to the United States at various times. Pueraria lobata is the variety that has a hammer lock on over 7,000,000 acres of land the Southeast.

Many older books identify kudzu as pueraria thunbergiana because this was the botanical classification used prior to 1947.

Other Names for Kudzu

Leaping over tall buildings, stopping speeding locomotives and capturing everything in its path, makes it impossible to ignore kudzu. This means people talk about it. They search for names to describe their observations and encounters with it. Long-winded Latin names are not sufficiently descriptive or colorful. The list continues to grow. Here are some of kudzu's names:

front porch vine
savior of southern soil
cuss you vine
mile a minute vine
that clinging vine
drop it and run vine
a miracle plant
eat you alive vine
rambunctious devil
an agricultural blessing
mindless, unkillable plant
a pest without equal
green scourge
invasive interloper
vegetative bulldozer
botanical nightmare
a curse
kudzu is right up there with death and taxes
a monstrosity
basket vine
a vine out of place
typical government gift
the vine that ate the south
perfect villain
best hay around
phoenix vine

Sodom vine
green gold
a tenacious weed
telephone vine
wonder vine
cosmic joke
foot a line vine
green menace
Jack and the Bean Stalk vine
monster vine
Godzilla vine
a vegetable form of cancer
a vine, but not divine
xxxx xxx xxxxx
xxxxxxxx
xxx xxxx xxxxxx - unprintable in this book!

One review of this list explains why kudzu is the vine to love or hate!

Chapter 2
Welcome to America

Kudzu made its first foray into American soil during the spring of 1876 at the United States Centennial Exposition in Philadelphia, Pennsylvania. Japan brought it to America and planted it at the Bazaar they erected to help celebrate America's first century as a country.

The Japanese Bazaar

This is a photograph of an etching of the Japanese Bazaar in Frank Leslie's Historical Register of the United States Centennial Exposition 1876, published in 1877.

When the Exposition opened on May 10, 1876, kudzu was just one plant among many. Within days, it became the center of attention because visitors could see it grow day to day. The word spread and people flocked to see it.

After seeing kudzu in bloom, Lily Romah wrote this note to her sister in Bonifay, Florida:

My dear Virgie,

Today I visited the Exposition. Of all the marvelous things there, a vine which the Japanese call kuzu astounded me most. It was almost as high as a porch ceiling with dark green leaves and the most beautiful purple flowers I have ever seen on a vine.

The hot afternoon air was fragrant with the aroma of grapes. There were no grapes in sight so I inquired. The kuzu flowers petals are small just like the ripe grapes on our old home place in New Jersey.

Knowing how you suffer from that awful heat down there, I am going to try to get one of these vines for you. I have the names of several nursery owners who told me they plan to sell it. I will write again soon but I want to post this today so you will be on the lookout for your kuzu vine. I miss you and love you.

Lily

July 23, 1876

(We appreciate T. B. McCall granting permission to print this letter. It is in his private collection of family papers.)

The Welcome Mat is Rolled Out

When the Exposition closed, the Japanese left kuzu with its American admirers. They rolled out the welcome mat and changed its name to 'kudzu.'

Between 1876 and 1902, the demand for kudzu never abated. During these years, most sales were through mail order catalogs. Buyers helped distribute kudzu as they learned to cut the vines and root them. During this period it was grown mainly as an ornamental vine. In most instances it was supported by some type of trellis. This inhibited normal reproduction through runners putting down roots from nodes. Consequently the problem of kudzu capturing everything in its path did not occur on a significant scale during its early years in America.

Perfect Habitat

Kudzu is native to Asia. It grows wild in Japan, China, Taiwan, Korea and India. In those countries it has native biological controls that keep it in check. Kudzu left these controls in Asia.

Nothing in America controls kudzu. Leaf-blight will attack it occasionally. Slugs and Japanese beetles have been known to stage raids. Rabbits and deer eat their fill without making a dent.

The warm moist climate in the Southeastern United States is the perfect habitat for kudzu. It grows better here than in anywhere in its native Asia. Mississippi, Alabama and Georgia have the most acres of kudzu.

Early Cautions About Kudzu

Just before the turn of the century, a few farmers in the South observed kudzu's penchant for dominance and refused to allow it on their land.

In 1902 David Fairchild, an employee of the United States Department of Agriculture, recognized kudzu's awesome potential for destruction. He had planted kudzu in his yard in Washington, DC and within a short time it was so rampant that he wanted rid of it. By constant effort he kept in check for several years but wrote that he failed to eradicate it completely.

David Fairchild spoke and wrote about his concerns over kudzu, but they were given little credence or publicity. They fell on deaf ears within the Department of Agriculture. This may explain why his cautions did not appear in print until 1938.

History has proven his concerns to be valid but they were too little and too late to lower the level of kudzu fever that was sweeping the country by that time.

Many persons, with admirable goals and insufficient botanical information, jumped into the fray and unleashed kudzu.

Chapter 3
Kudzu Zealots

Charles and Lillie Pleas were the first Kudzu Zealots. They were honored posthumously with this historical marker beside Highway 90 in Chipley, Florida for their devotion to the development of kudzu as an agricultural and soil saving plant.

Charles and Lillie Pleas: the First Kudzu Zealots

Charles and Lillie Pleas met kudzu in the front yard of their new home in Chipley, Florida just as the 20th Century began. There was not instant bonding between kudzu and the Pleas but once bonded, it was for life.

They were newlyweds from New Castle, Indiana. Chipley was a frontier-type town about the same age as the Pleas, twenty years old. Their new home was a small cottage called Glen Arden, a virgin timber and game preserve.

The Pleas immediately astounded the natives by talking about conserving soil, timber and wildlife at every opportunity. Persons who knew the Pleas have written that all this sounded a bit high-toned. Undaunted, they became Florida's first widely-known, dedicated conservationists.

Both the Pleas were well educated. Charles was a master photographer; Lillie was an artist. These talents were used to study and record samples of flora and fauna.

The Bonding

There are numerous anecdotal accounts, written by persons who knew them, about the Pleas/kudzu bonding. The dates in which this event is reported to have occurred vary from 1902 to 1904, as do the number of plants and the details of their first encounter. But the substance in each account of what happened is essentially the same.

The Pleas moved a few plants, which they had not identified, from their front yard and planted them around a trash pile to screen it from public view. In a very short time the vines covered the trash pile and crept through the bars of the horse shed. The horses ate what they could reach with gusto and rubbed the hair from their necks trying to get at the plant the Pleas would learn was kudzu.

The Pleas were Quakers and believed kudzu a miracle vine they should use to help humankind in a tangible way. To this end, they established Glen Arden Nursery to grow kudzu seedlings and root crowns. By the end of the second year, they had produced good quality crowns which they wanted to sell. It was difficult to remove the crowns from the soil without damaging them. Charles designed, and with the help of a local blacksmith, made a triangular plow which solved the problem. Production was increased but the expected customers did not materialize from the local population.

Simultaneously, the Pleas had planted several acres of kudzu to demonstrate its usefulness as a grazing and hay crop. They produced a bountiful crop of kudzu hay the first season with many vines over eighty feet long. Several local farmers bought the hay but were still too distrustful of any fine that grew as fast as kudzu to plant it on their land. The long, tough vines were difficult to harvest, and too much for the harvesting machinery that existed in the early 1900s.

Mail Order

The Pleas turned to mail order to sell kudzu. Their hyperbole about their miracle vine in sales literature and a pamphlet entitled *Kudzu - Coming Forage of the South* prompted the United States Post Office Department to investigate. The Pleas were suspected of using the mail to defraud the public. The investigation was short and closed quickly, with an apology, after an investigator came to Glen Arden Nursery and saw that kudzu grew just as advertised.

Charles Pleas is quoted as having said he knew how it felt to be a voice crying in the wilderness. Farmers and cattle ranchers who needed kudzu the most turned a deaf ear and blind eye. Kudzu could bring their dried up springs and ponds to life. It could prevent erosion. While other hay crops had to be planted annually and died in the blistering sun, kudzu flourished year after year. In times of drought, it could save the cattle and the cattle owner.

Lillie Pleas is quoted as using the Biblical metaphor to explain why people were not embracing kudzu. In any sowing, some seeds would fall upon stone, others upon fertile soil and flourish. She believed their divine task was to keep on sowing. And they did.

Their mail order sales were limited but steady. They were encouraged to hear about kudzu being exhibited in Jamestown, Virginia in 1907. When the Alabama Agricultural Experiment Station at Auburn expanded its study of kudzu in 1917, local sales increased slightly and there was a significant increase in mail order sales in Alabama.

In 1920, the Central of Georgia Railroad began buying kudzu plants, some from the Pleas, to give to farmers. The objective was to entice farmers to grow kudzu hay for the railroad to haul. The Railroad found few takers except those who used the plants to establish permanent pasture.

Vindication

In 1935, the Pleas had their faith in kudzu vindicated by the United States Government. Hugh Bennett, an advocate of soil conservation, was chosen as the first Chief of the new U. S. Soil Conservation Service. Cotton farming and road construction methods of the time had left the whole of the Southeast eroding away at an alarming rate. He chose kudzu as the plant to save the soil.

Charles and Lillie Pleas were ready with the kudzu crowns. They tried to get a contract to sell them to the Soil Conservation Service but failed. They were required to execute a performance bond but they did not have the money for a bond. It was a sad blow for them to see others who could execute the bond reap the economic benefits. But in keeping with their sense of mission, they rejoiced at the prospect of kudzu bringing real benefits to humankind.

Although the Pleas did not land a government contract to sell kudzu, the Glen Arden Nursery benefited from the kudzu planting frenzy that lasted from 1935 until the late 1940s. They continued their developmental and promotional work with kudzu, citing it at every opportunity as the plant that was saving the soil in the South. Charles Pleas had appeared before the Senate Agriculture Committee on several occasions and his efforts had been a factor in the Soil Conservation Service selecting kudzu.

The Pleas were bewildered why persons still refused to avail themselves of the benefits of kudzu after their government had investigated and chosen it to save the South. Leading publications such as *Time* and *The Readers Digest,* kept telling the world of this agricultural miracle but did not print any of the significant number of stories about the many problems kudzu growth was causing.

The Pleas heard about railroad cars sliding off the rails as the wheels crossed the heavy blankets of kudzu that had grown across the tracks. They also heard about abandoned homes being swallowed, forests being smothered and the numerous other problems their beloved vine was causing. Charles Pleas clung to the belief that only those who managed kudzu poorly experienced problems. Lillie Pleas is said to have pondered only what they could have done to develop kudzu differently.

Only the public's faith in kudzu had faltered. The Pleas left planet earth firmly believing their development of kudzu for agricultural use was their greatest contribution to the human family.

Hugh Hammond Bennett
A Zealot in Officialdom

Hugh Hammond Bennett has been described as the best friend kudzu ever had because he was at the right place at the right time. When he was appointed as Chief of the Soil

Conservation Service, he was a distinguished conservationist. He believed the devastating erosion of millions of acres of soil in the South had to be stopped and he decided to use kudzu to stop it. Most of the 7,000,000 acres of kudzu growing in the Southeast today are the direct result of the kudzu planting programs he created within the Soil Conservation Service and those he helped formulate within the U. S. Department of Agriculture and the Tennessee Valley Authority.

Between 1935 and 1942 millions, perhaps billions, of kudzu crowns and seedlings were planted by members of the Civilian Conservation Corps. The demand for kudzu exceeded the supply from private nurseries. The government established kudzu nurseries to fill the gap. They imported seeds from Japan and planted them in beds. As soon as they were pencil-size, they were shipped throughout the Southeast and planted on open land, along highways and railroads, and on gully banks.

Barren, dusty land turned lush green and stayed lush green each summer. Gullies disappeared. There was evidence at every turn that erosion was no match for kudzu.

Warnings

Even during the period of intense kudzu promotion and propagation, many scientists and technicians in and outside government agencies were sounding warning about the problems of kudzu overgrowth. The warnings went unheeded by government officials.

To sustain the momentum of kudzu planting, the Department of Agriculture paid as much as $8.00 an acre to landowners to plant it. In a depressed economy, this was a powerful incentive.

Hugh Hammond Bennett sent speakers throughout the Southeast to extol kudzu and distribute official publications which denounced fears of problems with overgrowth as unfounded if proper cultivation practices were followed. The States lent reinforcement to this position by publications by various colleges and agricultural departments. The Agricultural Experiment Station of the Alabama Polytechnic Institute had been experimenting with kudzu since the early 1900s. The Institute released a comprehensive summary of its findings in Circular 83 in December 1939. The question of kudzu becoming a pest by overgrowth was dismissed with this quoted paragraph:

KUDZU AS A PEST

Some farmers have opinions that kudzu may become a pest, may not be eradicated, and may spread into fields where it is not wanted. Such ideas are unfounded. It may be easily eradicated by grazing or by plowing. Kudzu has been confined to the edges of fields at Auburn for a period of 35 years and has never become a pest or spread to areas where it was not wanted. It may be confined indefinitely to terrace ridges in a field simply by cultivating the field in row crops.

Despite such pronouncements by zealots in officialdom, a substantial number of private landowners still trusted their eyes and experience. They did not believe what they were told and refused to plant kudzu.

Hugh Hammond Bennett's promotion of kudzu was a short term success by any measure. The jury is still out on the long term verdict.

Channing Cope
A Zealot in the Media

Channing Cope jumped on the kudzu bandwagon in the late 1930s and was its most flamboyant advocate for over ten years. Whether or not Channing Cope intended to simply capitalize on kudzu because he was a true zealot of its value, or a shrewd opportunist has been debated. He had a wide reputation for lacing his coffee with bourbon. Some close to him declare that there was a direct ratio between the amount of bourbon consumed and the ardor of his zeal that day for kudzu.

Channing Cope owned 700 acres of land in Covington, Georgia, which is just southeast of Atlanta. The land, he declared, was a wasteland until he discovered kudzu. That wasteland became Yellow River Farm, a showcase for kudzu.

He had a daily radio program on *WSB-AM* and wrote for the *Atlanta Journal-Constitution.* Many of his radio broadcasts were made from the front porch of his house at Yellow River Farm. He told his listeners and readers that kudzu had not only transformed good-for-nothing wasteland acres into a lush pasture land and prosperous farm, it was making him rich. The response to his kudzu gospel was immediate and positive.

Spellbound listeners and readers wanted to share in this miracle. A how-to book on getting rich with kudzu was a natural. He wrote *Front Porch Farming* and it was a hit. Over eighty thousand copies were sold. This, along with his already substantial following in the South, thrust him and the kudzu movement into the national spotlight for a brief time.

Pictures of Cope, fat, jovial-looking always, in a floppy straw hat, sent the message that not much human effort was required to raise cattle with kudzu. Some human effort, he conceded, was necessary to apply for the federal tax exemption.

Channing Cope founded the Kudzu Club of America in Atlanta and appointed himself president. At one time, there were reports of over 20,000 members in clubs across the country who met to promote planting kudzu.

The Kudzu Clubs of America offered a variety of fun activities for their members. Kudzu Queens were crowned, kudzu planting contests with prizes were held, and just for fun kudzu festivals swept the country until the late 1940s. Media coverage was extensive.

Cope Crowned Kudzu King

Cope loved the spotlight and the names members of the press bestowed upon him. He particularly like the titles, 'The Prophet' and 'Father of Kudzu,' but his favorite was 'Kudzu King.' He gained this title from his frequent proclamations that kudzu, not cotton, was king in the South.

If Channing Cope knew about the Pleas, it probably never occurred to him to defer any titles their way.

By the late 1940s, Kudzu was fast falling into disfavor with the public and the government. Reports of problems with kudzu tipped public opinion against it by 1950. In 1953, the government stopped recommending kudzu. Although his heyday as a kudzu zealot has passed, Cope was bitterly disappointed. He faded from the public arena and died in 1962. He was buried in an unmarked grave in Atlanta.

Post Cope Era at Yellow River Farm

After Channing Cope died, kudzu turned Yellow River Farm into a jungle and strangled the farmhouse. The porch from which he had told the world about kudzu became living evidence that kudzu grew as thick and fast as he said it did.

Bob Purser bought Yellow River Farm in 1976 with the intention of making it a productive enterprise despite the kudzu. Shortly after buying the farm, he was driving his four-wheel pick-up truck across a field of kudzu which looked solid. Without warning, his pick-up upended and came to rest at the bottom of a ravine. He was yanked from his seat and landed prone over the steering wheel. He escaped without serious injury and the steel bars he had installed across the front to protect the radiator kept damage to his pick-up to a minimum. He crawled out, vowing the kudzu traps had to go.

Although Bob Purser worked diligently at trying to eradicate kudzu, he could not. He kept it in check but it was still in control of several acres of Yellow River Farm when he sold it.

Cope's house at Yellow River Farm is falling down in 1996 - perhaps under the weight of the kudzu.

Chapter 4
A Memoir about Channing Cope and Charles and Nellie Pleas
By: Fisher L. Alberson

When I was a young man I read a book, *Front Porch Farming*, by Channing Cope. This Channing Cope was a disciple of kudzu and he proclaimed that 'kudzu was king.' He was the self-appointed president of the American Kudzu Society, preaching the wonders of this plant in a daily syndicated column on agriculture.

Cope called kudzu the cadillac of cow feeds. His theory was to set out a few plants, give them a little time, and you could rock on your front porch and watch your cattle eat and fatten. The idea of this lazy style of cattle raising fit right in with my thinking because I was already convinced that everybody should have a farm for the pleasure of seeing things grow and as a tax shelter.

I Took Channing Cope's Advice

I bought the farm. It was 100 acres of timberland, 50 acres of beautiful kudzu and 20 head of registered Black Angus. The rocking chair came next.

My dear reader, don't ever let it be said - as truth - that kudzu can't be done away with. Before I could take my rightful place in my rocking chair, the whole herd had eaten every sprig of kudzu down to its roots! Then my herd stood out in the middle of a barren field looking up ever so wistfully at the tallest vines that had found something to climb. They were trying to figure out a way to get at those vines!

This once beautiful herd had to be sold to a packing plant as cutters and canners at a giveaway price. It was either that or they would have starved to death. Who can take this kind of loss with a grin because of a tax shelter? Not me.

You know, those people who would have you believe they know about finances don't know anything at all. The tax exemption I finally got was chaotic beyond belief.

I never met Channing Cope but following his advice on cattle raising did not turn out to be one of the wiser choices I have made during my life.

I Remember the Pleas

I knew Mr. and Mrs. C. E. (Charles and Lillie) Pleas when I was a young boy in Chipley, Florida. They lived in a wooded tract of land on the Vernon Highway near the Daring Mill. They created a rustic Garden of Eden on the place.

They were artists, taxidermists, animal lovers, experts on horticulture, ornithology and herpetology and most anything else worthwhile that dealt with the wonders of nature and God's creations. Their property was a game preserve with all virgin timber.

The Pleas enjoyed children and always welcomed Boy Scouts and other youth groups. As a small boy I enjoyed many pleasant hours with Mr. Pleas. They had a pet snake that had the run of the yard, and I remember seeing it many times in a flower bed or sunning on the front porch.

One of the Pleas' prime interests was to develop kudzu as an conservation plant and believed it to be a grand plant to provide food for animals.

Years later, as an adult, I read a column by the late Ralph McGill, Atlanta Constitution Editor, devoted to Cope and kudzu. Cope had Ralph McGill convinced of the virtues of kudzu. At the end of the column was a question: "I wonder if the national president of the American Society of Kudzu knows that the father of kudzu, as we know it in this country, was C. E. Pleas of Chipley, Florida?"

I sent a copy of the column to Earl Sellers who, in turn, passed it on to Mr. Pleas. Shortly thereafter, I received a long letter from Mr. Pleas giving me the full details of his work with kudzu and his several trips to Washington to appear before the Senate Agriculture Committee to promote kudzu.

Before Mr. Pleas passed away in 1954, he was fully aware of the numerous problems his beloved plant had created for farming in general.

With all of this, Mr. Pleas may still be rewarded for all his efforts and dreams for kudzu. Research has found that kudzu lowers the blood pressure in animals. Scientists are experimenting to see if it does the same in humans.

Mr. and Mrs. Pleas were one of the most interesting couples I have ever known. They were from the North and adopted Chipley as their home. Having seen kudzu under their control may have made me much more receptive to Channing Cope's message about it than I might otherwise have been.

Mr. Fisher L. Alberson lived in Chipley, Florida most of his life.
In 1996, he is retired and lives in Lithonia, Georgia.
We appreciate his allowing us to print this memoir.

KUDZU KLASS

Kudzu Roots often weigh between 400 and 500 pounds. These roots are full of high quality starch. It is extracted and ground into powder for use in cooking. The powder is an excellent thickening ingredient for puddings, sauces, and confections. It can also be used as a medicine. Four ounces of imported kudzu powder sells for $4.95. Why are you, kudzu patch owner, not figuring out a way to dig up this white gold?

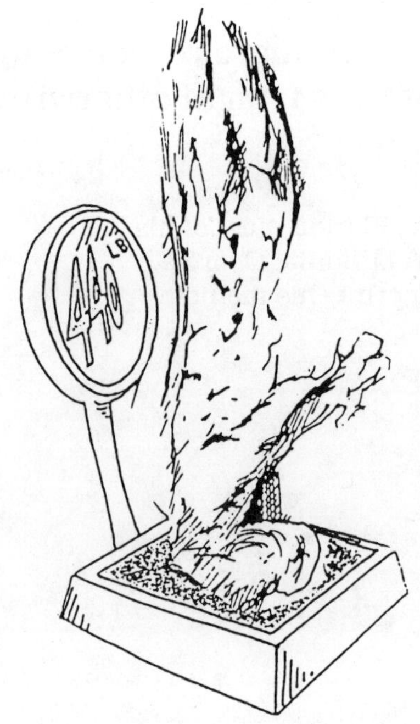

Chapter 5
Disillusionment

Most of the public was disillusioned with kudzu by the late 1940s. It was under siege for doing exactly what the Kudzu Zealots had said it would do: grow fast, in any type soil, resist drought, and live forever. Problems caused by excessive growth could not be ignored. Official reports were made to the Department of Agriculture, and other government agencies, from many segments of the Southeast.

Railroads

Railroad engineers reported dangerous situations on the rails where kudzu had covered them. As the wheels passed over the kudzu the leaves and vines were ground to a slick pulp. This caused the train to slip dangerously and sometimes derail on steep grades. Also, the kudzu kept the ties and rails wet much of the time. This increased maintenance costs as did the alternative of keeping it off the railroads.

Farmers

Many of the farmers who had accepted the government payment to plant kudzu asked for help in getting rid of it. Kudzu was the most formidable plant enemy they had ever encountered and they were losing good farm fields to it at an alarming rate. All buildings were at risk. Many crop and cattle farmers declared they had been tricked into trading the devil for a witch.

Foresters

The United States Forest Service, and private foresters, reported that kudzu was killing hundreds of trees each season by climbing them and smothering them to death. No seedlings for new trees could grow because the sun could not penetrate through the thick kudzu . Snakes and several types of burrowing animals multiplied beneath the kudzu canopy. Their presence increased the danger of working with trees.

Public Utility Companies

Public utility companies reported kudzu climbed their poles faster than they could go from pole to pole to cut it down. The kudzu vines caused the lines to short out electrical service to part or all of a community.

Highway Departments

Kudzu had been planted on road embankments and did stop erosion as it was intended to do. But it also covered the pavement if traffic was not heavy, obscured road signs faster than the workers could uncover them, and killed every tree it was allowed to climb.

Private Citizens

Private citizens complained about the inconvenience they suffered because of the problems reported by the various segments of the economy. Those who had kudzu on their property, but had not suffered personal damage from it, saw what it could do, and wanted to know how to get rid of it as a precaution.

Many persons applied for tax relief because their property had been rendered useless under the kudzu and the cost of eradicating it was beyond their means. Counties were reluctant to grant relief, and in many cases the owners simply abandoned the land because it was lost anyway.

Government Reaction

Because the United States Government had been the prime promoter of kudzu, citizens demanded help with the problems that no one had warned them to anticipate.

In 1953 all Departments of the United States Government reacted by stopping advocating the use of kudzu, but had no new suggestions for controlling it.

In 1972, the United States Department of Agriculture declared kudzu to be a weed, but, as in 1953, had no new suggestions for controlling it.

No relief program for private citizens who have suffered financial losses because of kudzu has ever been undertaken by the U. S. Government or any state government.

The problems kudzu causes are very easy to identify. Their solution seems far into the future. But ours is a creative, capitalistic society. Someone figured out how to send astronauts to the moon and how to travel regularly in space. Someone will either find a high quantity, profitable use for kudzu or find its Achilles heel.

KUDZU KLASS

Kudzu leaves grow in a pattern of three on a slim, strong stalk that is between 3 and 6 inches in length. When they first appear they are tiny and a delicate shade of green on top, silvery on the underside. They retain the slivery lining but the top deepens to a dark shade of lush green. If you intend to make earrings, as has been done with two genuine kudzu leaves pictured below. You can pick small leaves for small earrings or big leaves for *BIG* earrings!

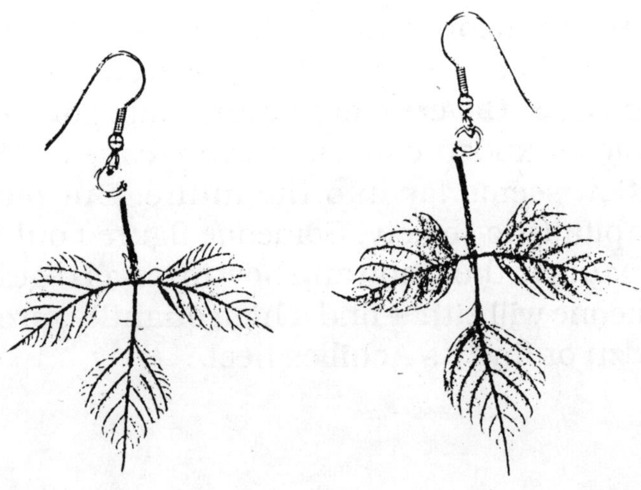

Part II

Kudzu Arts and Crafts

Chapter 6
How to Make a Round Kudzu Basket
By: Diane Hoots

The basic skills acquired in making a basket will be useful in coaxing kudzu vine into a myriad of beautiful, and useful, items. Selecting good vines and *patience* are the requirements for success and joy in working with kudzu.

Selecting the Kudzu Vines

If you do not own the land from which you wish to harvest kudzu vines, be sure to ask permission; no one had ever said no to me!

Winter is the best time to harvest kudzu vines for basket making. However, if you harvest in summer or fall, be aware of the biting and stinging creatures, including snakes, that make their home in kudzu patches.

A sharp pruner or knife is essential. Find a patch of kudzu where the vines are growing up a tree. These vines are cleaner because they have no roots and are thicker than those growing along the ground. Select brown, flexible vines. Avoid stiff, dead vines. Green (new growth) vines are brittle, making it harder to use in the basket. They also have a tendency to mildew and shrink because of the higher water content.

To harvest a vine, cut it at ground level and pull from the tree. This may require considerable force and be alert to avoid falling tree limbs and other debris. Harvest vines of different thicknesses. While you are in the kudzu patch, harvest an ample supply.

Vines harvested during the growing season are better if left to dry a day or two before attempting to work with them.

Cutting the Vines for the Basket

Determine the size basket you want to make. Then cut 5 (6 for larger baskets) lengths of vine from the thickest, most flexible kudzu vines. The length should be twice the dimension of the outside of the basket; measure by following the guides (> <} shown in this diagram:

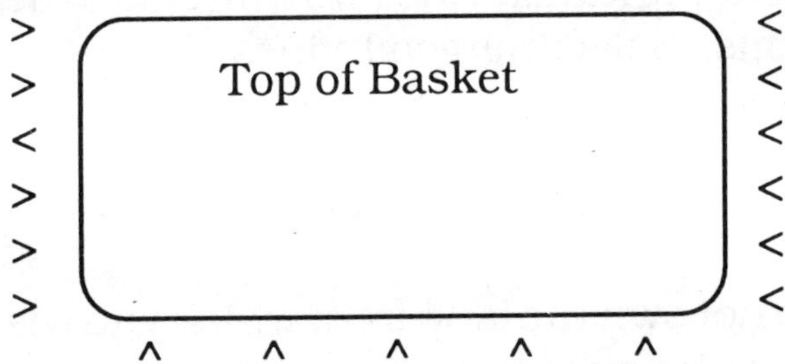

One segment of vine should be cut slightly over half the length of the others.

Begin Weaving the Basket

Lay 3 of the long vine segments parallel. At their center, cross with the remaining long segments. Now place the shorter segment between the two segments on top extending one end slightly beyond the three segments on the bottom as shown in the Photo Number 1 on the next page.

Using the thinnest, longest and strongest vine, tie the 6 long segments together, going over the top 3 and under the bottom 3 about three times.

Do NOT cut the vine as it will be used in weaving the basket. Make sure the vine segments are tightly secured and centered; see the Photo Number 2 on the next page.

Photo Number 1

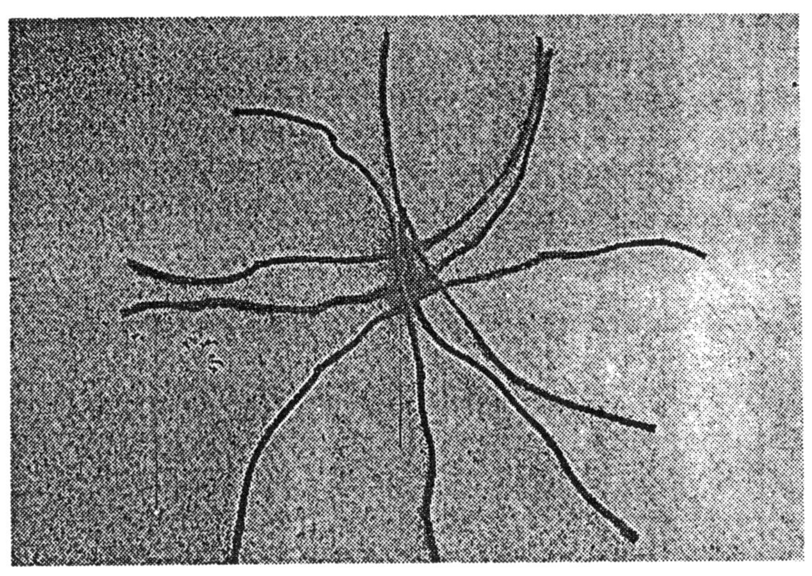

Photo Number 2

Caution: Do not weave around this

The sections of vines radiating from the center are the spines of the basket. Note there are a odd number of spines. This was accomplished by adding the one short segment that is required for the weaving that follows.

Spread the spines so that they are evenly spaced like the spokes of a wagon wheel. Use the remainder of the vine used to secure the segments to start weaving. Weave by alternately placing the vine over and then under the spines, pulling tightly and pushing down to prevent gaps. When weaving correctly, each time a spine is reached the vine should be on the opposite (over or under) side. If a weaving mistake is made, unwind the vine to the mistake and continue.

Caution: the short extension of the original half segment becomes part of the spine next to it. DO NOT weave around it separately as this will result in an even number of spines.

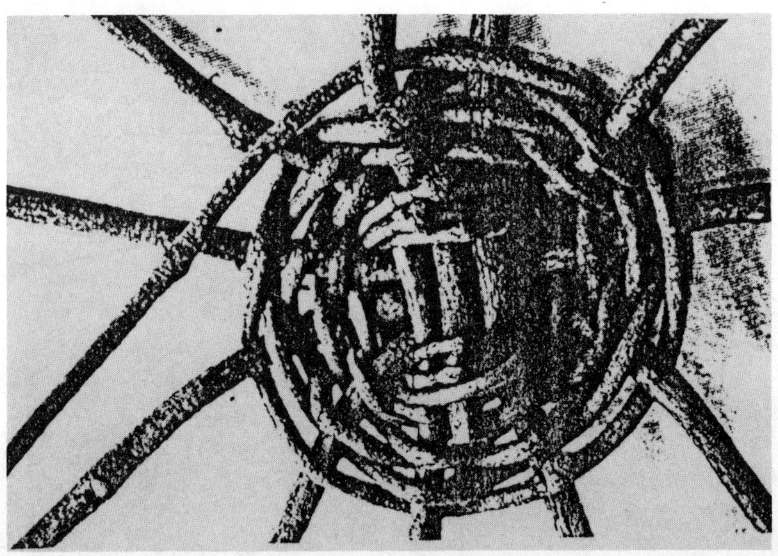

When the end of a weaving vine is reached, lay another weaving vine of approximately the same thickness so that it overlaps the previous weaving vine for a distance of at least one spine, then continue weaving. This secures both weaving vines. Weave until the desired diameter (width) of the basket is reached.

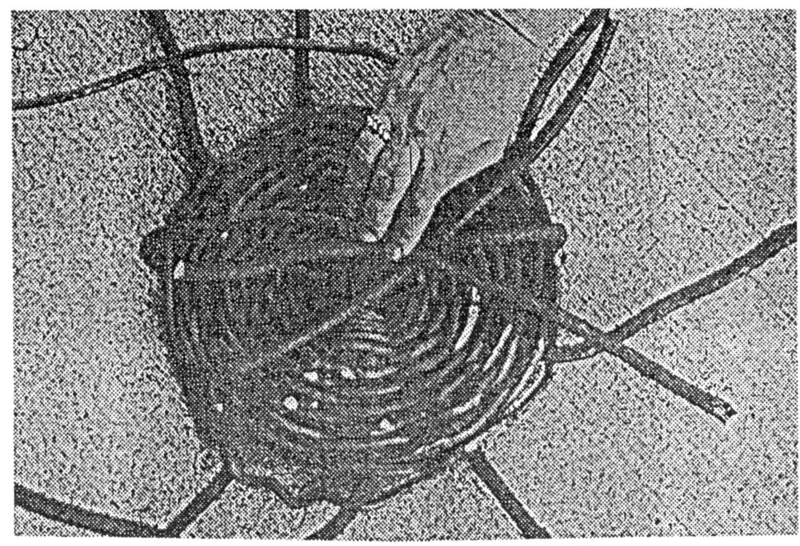

Fold over and crease all spines in an upward direction. Continue weaving up the side of the basket until the desired basket depth is reached. Be sure not to weave more than approximately one third of the distance up the spine. Sufficient spine length is required in the next step to tuck.

One way to finish the basket is to use the scalloped tuck pattern.

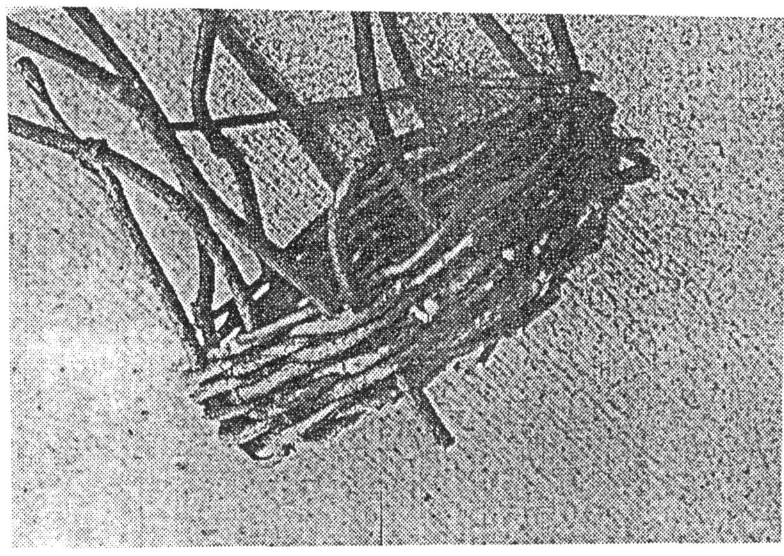

Start the tuck by bending a spine past one spine and pushing it through the space beside the third spine. Now tuck the skipped spine (second) beside the fourth spine. Continue until all spines are tucked.

Most often tucking a spine through the space beside another spine is a difficult task. Screwdrivers and/or needle-nose pliers can be used to push and pull the vines to make tucking easier. Cutting the ends of the spines on a diagonal also helps for easier tucking. Pull the tucker end of all the spines until the desired scallop is achieved at the top of the basket and all vines are tucked into place.

Cut the excess spine from the bottom of the basket. The basket can be shaped before the vines dry completely by applying appropriate pressure. Let the basket dry before using it.

If you want a handle on your basket, you can add it after all spines are tucked. Cut a piece of twisted, curled or braided vine twice as long as you want the handle. Push (using tools) the end down one spine and up the next, forming a 'u' to secure it. Repeat on the other side.

Diane Hoots is pulling kudzu vines. She will turn these vines into baskets, such as those she is displaying in the photo below.

Matthew Hoots is seated beside his kudzu teddy bear which won first place at the Georgia National Fair in October 1994, when he was 18. He made the basket he is holding when he was 9

Bryan Bonwich, age 15, of Warner Robins, Georgia is holding the first kudzu basket he ever made. Voila!

Chapter 7
Cherokee Basketmaker and Fiber Artist, Nancy Basket

Nancy Basket is a contemporary Cherokee basketmaker and fiber artist. She takes her name from the work she does, as did her great-great-great grandmother, Margaret Basket. She holds artisan status in the International Guild of Miniature Artisans for her true miniature baskets where 1" = 1'. She is an approved artist in basketry, papermaking and storytelling in North and South Carolina.

Nancy's work with kudzu began in 1989. She now shares her Native American heritage by retelling ancient legends orally and through her kudzu art. Many of her cards illustrate Native American ideographs and symbols that in themselves tell stories.

Here is Nancy's story in her own words.

My Connection to Kudzu
By: Nancy Basket

My family and I moved south in 1989 to a town that had hosted a Kudzu Festival for 15 years. I was asked to turn the notorious vine, kudzu, into baskets. I pulled the vines, worked them into a resemblance of a basket and in just a few days they fell apart! Knowing the error of my ways, I returned to the kudzu patch and apologized. We Cherokee people believe that everything has a spirit and should be respected. I gave the plants a gift of tobacco and said I would stay in the field until they told me how they wanted to be used. After a while I received the definite impression that kudzu vines wanted to be used for paper, and that the trees needed to be left alone.

I knew that cotton has been used in paper production for centuries. But I enjoy gathering my own materials and cotton fields were not close to me. Kudzu being everywhere, I knew where to get an inexhaustible supply but needed more information on the exact science of papermaking. I then consulted more "talking leaves" - books. Native people thought Europeans were very connected to the Great Spirit as many of them could "read leaves" and only a few of our medicine people could do that!

The books in the library said that a plant source is ground into pulp, suspended in a vat of water, and gathered on a screen to make a sheet of paper. It is then transferred from the screen to a cloth, pressed in a vice and left to dry under stacks of newspaper. Well here in the south, that can take days to dry, the paper often molds, and the texture of the paper is always smooth. Being a quilter since high school, I was interested in paper designs that could more simulate the woven texture of fabric, as I didn't have time to do the hand stitching anymore.

A $4,000 machine called a Hollander beater chews fiber into pulp. I substituted an old Vita Mix blender that did wonders for the pulp after the kudzu was cooked for many hours on the stove with water to cover. After the children thought I was going to make them eat the cooked kudzu, I was relegated to the outdoors. I soon found that cooking 15 pounds of green kudzu leaves outside for eight hours in the hot summer sun was rather undesirable! So I figured out the leaves could just be placed in water to cover and they would break down by themselves in a couple of weeks. It worked! My first cooked 100% kudzu pulp was hairy and didn't hold together well. The addition of 25% recyclable paper in the form of mat board or shredded computer paper seemed to be the right combination. "Rotting" kudzu

A Handmade/Hand-Assembled Kudzu Card by Nancy Basket

can almost be used without additional paper. The smell is so atrocious and long lasting, however, that my family made a perfume from the kudzu blossom to hide the stench until it could wear off. Even hard scrubbing could not remove it. Oh, the price of art!

I read about stretching mesh wire over wooden frames. When I made a couple of these deckles, they warped and twisted when used in water for a while. I began using plastic needlepoint canvas stiffener for the deckle and found the texture the screen left in the dried paper made it look like woven fabric. This was perfect for the quilt patterns.

My Life Changed When I Listened to Kudzu

My life changed when I listened to Kudzu. I started selling my kudzu quilt designs all over the United States through a national representative. I became an artist in education making kudzu paper with South Carolina students in public schools, kindergarten through high school. After respecting the kudzu, I eventually learned to split the vine and coiled kudzu basketry was added to the list of school choices. My first presentation is Native American storytelling for the entire student body. As our students remember about respect for all things, even plants, they find a new attitude for themselves and others and our world becomes a much better place.

Great Food - Kudzu!

What else can you do with kudzu? Eat it! Kudzu cuisine fascinates family and friends and dominates church socials. The taste of raw, small leaves is that of green beans as the plant is in the legume family. These little leaves are delicious in a marinated salad with onions and tomatoes, covered with Italian dressing.

Steam a cup of small leaves, chop them up and put them in your favorite pasta dough ingredients. Slip the dough into the pasta maker and you have green kudzu pasta. With the addition of marinana sauce, you have a healthy entree with a great amount of protein.

Dry and crumble small leaves into muffins, breads or melted almond bark with nuts and raisins and you have 'healthy' candy, kid-tested!

A variety of teas can be made from the steeped purple blossoms of the kudzu flower. Pour boiling water on top of a gallon of fresh picked kudzu blossoms. Steep overnight and remove the new colorless petals. Mix the reddish purple liquid with white grape juice and a variety of herbal teas for a refreshingly different summer drink.

Move over mint julep! My friends, Jim and Peggy Waller, own an antebellum bed and breakfast called The Inn at Merridum here in Union, South Carolina. We have been known to sit on their huge pilloried porch and sip the kudzu on occasion. I've heard that kudzu wine is mighty fine. You never know what secret ingredient Peggy and Jim put in their famous blueberry pancakes!

Collaborating With Other Artists

My current kudzu project involves a collaboration with other artists. When I split kudzu vines for baskets, many fine thread-like lengths appear in the older thicker vines. I gave these threads to my friends Suzanne and Dusty Rine, spinners and weavers on Edisto Island. I met the Rines through the South Carolina Artisans' Center in Walterboro at a Hands-On Demonstration, where I am a juried artist and board member. These mini fairs, held in the spring and fall of the year, feature artists showing the public what we do and how we do it.

As we watched, Suzanne and Dusty spun and wove the kudzu fibers I had given them into a course cloth! The cloth, as yet, is only a sample, but oh, the possibilities! This summer I'll experiment with the Oriental method of fermenting young vines in an earthen pit lined with grass clippings. This procedure will separate the kudzu fiber into much finer threads, that when tied together, can be woven into fabric finer than silk. I can see the Southern cloth industry revitalized by making kudzu vine like silk and linen.

This summer as my old barn is restored for use as a studio, the back portion will be rebuilt with kudzu bales purchased from Edith and Henry Edwards who grow kudzu hay in North Carolina. Chicken wire will cover the bales, poles will be inserted through them for reinforcement and a stucco coating will be applied on the outside. Then I will have room to experiment more with 4' by 8' three dimensional, kudzu paper wall hangings. Since the kudzu grows on one side of my 10 acres, it behooves me to use it in all the ways I can as quickly as possible. If we started a root starch factory in the barn, the by-product is cellulose fiber to use in paper, or maybe we could use it to reinforce cardboard so that more in turn could be recycled. But as I am known to say...that's another story.

Nancy Basket and her children cooking kudzu to make paper before she learned the leaves would break down by themselves.

Other Accomplishments

Nancy was commissioned to make Iroquois masks for the movie *The Last of the Mohicans*. As South Carolina welcome stations are being redesigned, her work is being displayed in them.

She contributed two chapters to a Storey Publications book *Natural Baskets*. The chapters give instructions for making several types of baskets, and as a bonus she weaves Cherokee stories into her instruction.

Asked how she came to continue making kudzu baskets after her initial trial, she replies, "Once I made my first basket, I knew it was something I would do for the rest of my life. Native American people call this 'finding the red road' and I have found my 'red road' here, close to my tribe's reservation in Cherokee, North Carolina.

Nancy Basket

KUDZU KLASS

Kudzu seed production begins when kudzu plants are three years old. The seeds are in a flat beanlike pod covered with a very heavy coat of fine downy hair. The pod is green until ripe, then turns dark brown.

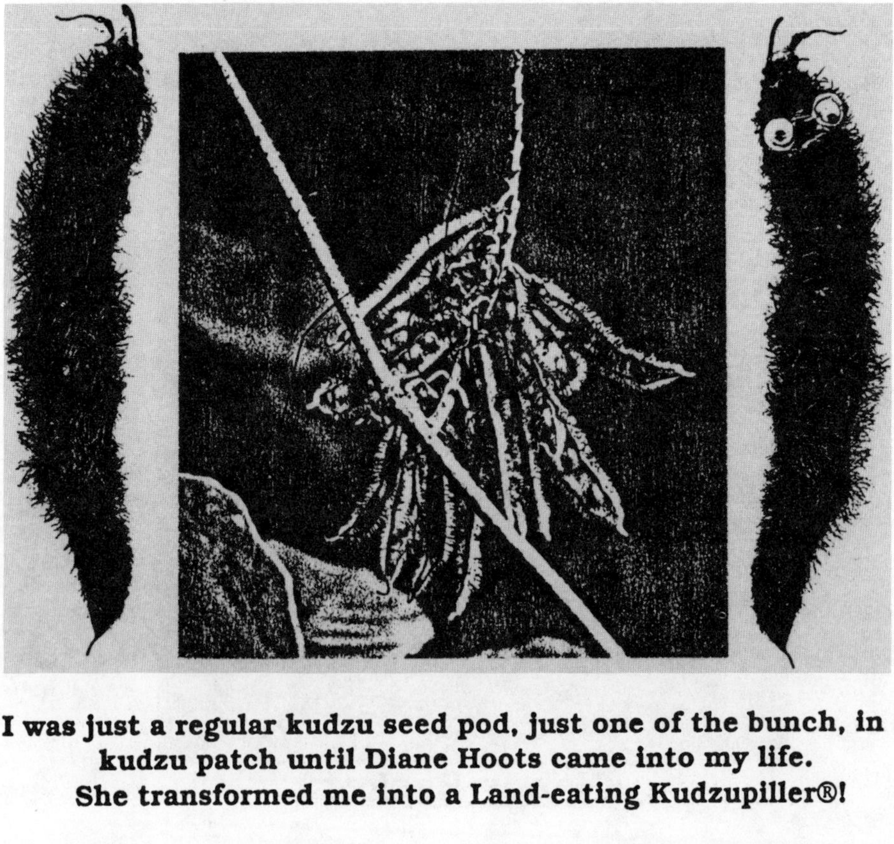

I was just a regular kudzu seed pod, just one of the bunch, in a kudzu patch until Diane Hoots came into my life. She transformed me into a Land-eating Kudzupiller®!

Chapter 8
Natural Materials Artisan, Ruth Duncan

Ruth Duncan of Greenville, Alabama transforms natural materials most people throw away, or consider useless, into a myriad of utilitarian and decorative items. What began as an interest has mushroomed into a full time craft business called Kudzu Kountry, much to her surprise and delight.

Ruth's experience appears to confirm the adage that there is no such thing as a little decision. Kudzu Kountry really began when Ruth took a basic basket weaving course at Auburn University in 1986. There she learned to weave round, square and egg baskets using reed. Kudzu, she decided after finishing the course, was a superior vine and taught herself to use it. Apparently others agree on kudzu's superior qualities because she has won numerous awards for her kudzu baskets. Among them are a first place award at Festival-in-the-Park show in Montgomery, and one at the Butler County Fair in Greenville.

After perfecting the use of kudzu vine, much of Ruth's early work was with kudzu and acorns. She made miniature houses which were, in many cases, custom duplicates of the buyers' home. She also makes flowers from the tender inner shucks of corn. A very intensive labor endeavor, she says.

Kudzu baskets are now her forte. She weaves, on average, about a hundred baskets each year. They range in size from tiny to large enough for an adult to sit in.

Ruth says kudzu baskets are durable and the vine texture of each is unique. "In fact," she said, "they last so long that I stopped spraying them with any kind of preservative long ago. Folks want them in the rough, just the way they turn out."

A Puzzle about Basket Weaving Remains

Ruth weaves the handle and rim of a basket first. Next, she uses a technique called a "god's eye" to anchor the assembly. She was so curious about the term "god's eye" that she launched a search several years ago for its meaning. The best information she has to date is that it is an Indian term but is not confident that is correct.

As of June 1996, she has not found authentic information as to the actual origin of the term. She, and the authors of this book, would like to hear from anyone who knows the true origin of the term "god's eye" and its original meaning.

Public Speaking

Also, quite unexpectedly, Ruth added public speaking to her repertoire. She speaks for civil groups, garden clubs and is often interviewed for articles about her work that appear in the printed and visual media.

She says she often get comments of appreciation following a speech for her light-hearted approach. Many of these groups have speakers on vital subjects such as child and drug abuse, domestic violence and income tax. Hearing about kudzu is a welcome break.

One of her favorite stories she tells her audiences is about a Yankee passing through North Carolina. The Yankee admired kudzu and asked if it would grow up North. The North Carolinian assured the Yankee that it would if proper procedures were followed.

The Yankee asked, "Will you tell me what they are?"

The proper procedures were given with a straight face. "Get yourself a good load of kudzu vines, burn them on concrete, plant the ashes and it will not only come up, but flourish."

One of Ruth's poems about kudzu, *Catch Me if You Can,* is in this book in the chapter entitled, A Kudzu Anthology.

Ruth's plans are to continue making kudzu baskets until either she or kudzu gives out. With kudzu's track record, it is not likely to give out.

Ruth Duncan is sitting in one of her large kudzu baskets.

Catch me if You Can
By: Ruth Duncan

Way up in the Northeast, where they have lots of snow,
They planted some kudzu, but it would not grow.
Down here in Alabama and all across the Southland,
The kudzu is thriving, saying 'Catch Me if You Can!'

Our climate is more perfect for it to go on it's way,
Than anywhere else in the world, so the scientists say.
It covers all it touches, from houses to cars,
And the way it keeps growing, it will soon reach Mars.

They say in a day, we can harvest a ton,
And the best way to plant it is, throw it down and run.
You are lucky if you don't have kudzu on your land,
'Cause it is thriving, saying 'Catch Me if You Can.'

Chapter 9
Kudzu Artist, Regina Hines

For sixteen years, Regina Hines of Ball Ground, Georgia has been weaving unique baskets, birdhouses, framed mirrors, cornucopias, and other useful and beautiful creations, from kudzu vines. Although she uses wild grapevines, honeysuckle, and wisteria, kudzu is her favorite because it is the most flexible and versatile. Her work is in demand as accessories for many styles of interiors, to spotlight as sculptural art and as unique hand-woven gifts from Georgia. Regina's success as a Kudzu Artist resulted from her decision to do something positive with kudzu.

Regina Hines weaving a random weave basket.

Drawing upon a rich background of exposure to all the fiber arts while growing up, it has never occurred to Regina Hines to attend classes for learning her craft. She relies instead on the valuable lessons learned from experience.

Here is her story.

Kudzu Imparts Serenity

By: Regina Hines

My weaving began at the retirement farm of a sister-in-law in Lineville, Alabama, which she had named "The Kudzu" for reasons immediately obvious to any visitor. Becoming weary of the moaning, groaning and complaining, I decided to do something positive with kudzu.

We went out that Fall and made wreaths. During our gathering, I noticed the nice thicker vines and determined I would see what kind of baskets could be woven with them. The results were a variety of random-weave baskets, no two of which looked alike. I am still working with that original design and even today, random weave baskets form a large part of my production.

Free Form and Traditional Baskets by Regina Hines

Resembling "instant antiques," all they needed was marketing and soon they were available in antique shops north of Atlanta and I was shipping them to areas further away.

I have always done most of my own vine gathering, taking advantage of the opportunities to enjoy the solitude of the woodlands. There are pitfalls to be avoided, including the deep, almost invisible holes left by rotted out trees. It is entirely possible to step into one of those up to the hip!

Of course, there are poison ivy and insects, but they take a back seat to other critters. Ground hogs and weasels emerge from their large holes, very surprised to see a human but fortunately scurry off in search of food and water.

Folk-art Christmas tree with recycled tin star (Photo credit: Bryan White)

I assume that the snakes must retreat from the earth-shaking noise I make but I do dress appropriately. Once a "critter" jumped from a nearby tree onto my shirtsleeve,giving me quite a scare until I looked down and realized it was a little 'ole tree frog. Then there are times when I am pulling away at a particularly stubborn vine and suddenly it lets go and I am sent sprawling. Thank heavens the kudzu patch is soft!

My work has been exhibited at many locations including Artworks Gallery, Seattle, Washington; DeKalb Council for the Arts in Dunwoody; and in a one-person show at Emory University, Atlanta, Georgia, and permanently at the West Point Georgia Welcome Center. Houston's Restaurants have used my designs all over the United States.

The State of Georgia commissioned me to weave over one hundred baskets each May of 1985, 1987, 1988 and 1989. These were brought to Washington, D.C. and presented to legislators during National Tourism week. In 1989, I was invited to accompany my baskets and demonstrate weaving them. The highlight of that trip was the extensive interview which was conducted by the Voice of America (Indonesian branch). I teach workshops at many institutions, among them are Etowah Indian Mounds, Cartersville, Georgia and John C. Campbell Folk School in Brasstown, North Carolina.

Kudzu Birdhouse with honeysuckle perches, yes, it functions. (Photo credit: Bryan White)

I have been interviewed by many television networks, including NPR Victory Garden in the South, NHK Japan Today, and Alabama Public Television.

My work has received notice in the Atlanta Journal, local newspapers, as well as the Athens and Charlotte Magazines. Also, I am a frequent speaker for garden clubs, schools and art councils. I am currently weaving five different techniques with kudzu but I realize there are two or three additional ones that could be done if only there were more hours in the day. That is what keeps me absorbed full-time, regarding kudzu as a medium that offers endless exploration. Gathering the vines and weaving with kudzu imparts to me a wonderful sense of serenity and oneness with the universe and its creator. I plan to keep on weaving with kudzu, of course!

Chapter 10
Artist Working in Book Arts, Rajeania Snider

Rajeania Snider of Rockford, Tennessee has been working professionally as a papermaker since 1978 when she joined the Foothills Craft Guild in Oak Ridge, Tennessee. It began when she read an article on papermaking in *Mother Earth News* in 1976 and ordered a booklet they offered for sale. From there on she started making paper for stationery, collage, and book binding. She has a Bachelor of Fine Arts in Graphic Design from the University of Tennessee and until 1976 she had focused on printmaking, mostly relief, silkscreen and letterpress. Here is her story.

Papermaking
By: Rajeania Snider

I am mainly self-taught, though I have taken a few workshops in the last three years to hone my skills. Once I got hooked on papermaking, it led to my making contacts with people in that and related fields that also got me into bookbinding.

Kudzu is a bast fiber and is one of the more difficult to prepare. I boil it with soda ash for six to eight hours. It is then rinsed and hand beaten until the fibers separate easily. I will rinse it again and then begin running it in the blender. Sometimes I will hand beat it again and then run it through the blender a second time. There are times when I have to repeat this for a third time as well. Occasionally there are a few stubborn bits that the only solution is to pick them out.

Sometimes I have access to a Hollander. When I use it I do not hand beat but run it in the Hollander for about an hour to an hour and a half, lowering the rollers every fifteen to twenty minutes until it is beaten to the fineness I want.

A Hollander, as you have concluded, is a machine for beating fibers into pulp. For those readers who may be considering papermaking, this is a brief explanation of this machine that saves lots of hand labor.

A Hollander that would be satisfactory to beat kudzu would cost close to $4,000. Most commercially available beaters are intended to be used on wood pulps or other fibers for which entanglement is not a problem.

The capacity of a beater is determined by the weight of dry fiber to the weight of water. A one and one half pound beater can accommodate one and one half pounds of dry fiber in forty-eight pounds, or six gallons, of water. This concentration will affect the character of the resulting pulp. Higher concentrations - that is, more fiber - will increase the amount of cutting that occurs during the beating. Lower concentrations increase the amount of fibrillation that occurs. A well-fibrillated pulp will produce a denser, stronger, more translucent sheet than a pulp whose fibers are over-shortened and less fibrillated.

One pound of beaten pulp will produce approximately seventy-five sheets of eight-by-eleven stationery-weight paper. After removing the pulp from the Hollander, it is ready to use for sheet forming. The season in which the kudzu is gathered will affect the color of the paper. Fresh green plant material will have a greenish cast to it, dried material will be a tan color.

A freshly made sheet of paper is known as wetleaf or waterleaf. It is a porous web of cellulose waiting to absorb any liquid applied to it - paint, ink, oily fingerprints. This receptive characteristic of the sheet has caused problems for papermakers, printers, calligraphers, and artists. Since early times many different materials have been used to counteract this absorbency.

Substances are added to the vat before the sheet is formed or applied to the finished paper, and processes have been developed to rub and polish the surface of the sheets.

Fillers are finely ground, nonfibrous materials, usually minerals, that are added to the pulp near the end of the beating process. They do not penetrate the fiber but coat its surface. Consequently, they make the paper less durable by decreasing its bonding capacity. Fillers settle on and between the fibers, closing the pores of the sheet and producing a smooth surface. They make the paper opaque, heavier and less absorbent.

Sheet Formation

When enough pulp has been prepared to the quality you need, stir until the fibers are evenly dispersed. Stirring will be necessary before dipping each sheet.

A deckle, which is a frame around the edges of a mold, is used to form the sheets of paper. Holding the deckle and mold together dip into the upper end of the vat, pull forward and submerging completely. Level off then lift slowly to the surface and give a slight shake to evenly spread the fibers. Lift out of the vat, tilt and drain. Remove the deckle, lay the mold pulp side down on a felt. This is called couching. Cover this with another piece of felt and continue alternating paper and felt until out of pulp.

This stack of paper and felt is called a post. The post is pressed to remove as much water as possible Each sheet may be transferred to a dry felt and pressed again. From here, the sheets are removed from the felts and stacked to dry. They may be gently ironed dry between pieces of cotton muslin after the second pressing, if desired. Once dry, the sheets are ready to be used.

Uses for Kudzu Paper

As mentioned, sheets of freshly made paper are called waterleaf, sometimes wetleaf. Good paper is really made during the preparation. If you want fine smooth sheets it takes time to work the pulp to the consistency that is required. Botanical papermakers learn to give the time or turn to other pursuits!

Once made to a quality that is acceptable to me, I use it for a variety of things. What I sell as a production line is stationery, blank page books, albums, miniature book earrings and pins, and I make marbeled barrettes and stationery.

I also do special orders. In 1995, I designed marbled end papers for the University of Tennessee Yearbook. I do traditional Turkish watercolor marbling on my handmade paper as well as commercial paper. Last year I purchased two small letter presses so I will be able to set my own type and print my books at home.

On-Hands Papermaking in Japan

True paper was developed in China by a court official around the year 104 A.D. and was a guarded secret for thousands of years. Recent archeological findings show evidence of papermaking being even older.

Any cellulose fiber will make paper but not all fibers will make a paper of archival quality. Different types of plant fibers produce varying amount of pulp. There are three fibers usable for papermaking: leaf, grass and bast. As mentioned earlier, kudzu is a bast fiber, the hardest to prepare but produce the most fiber.

From September 27 through October 8, 1995, I went to Japan with a group organized by Marilyn Sward, Director of the Books Arts Program at Columbia College in Chicago and Timothy Barrett an American authority on Japanese papermaking. Tim has written a book on the subject. There were 19 professional papermakers in the group. We attended the International Paper Symposium and annual meeting of IAPMA (International Artists and Papermakers Association) October 3 - 7. Prior to the meeting, we visited two papermaking centers.

First we went to Kurodani, a papermaking cooperative in the foothills of the mountains near Kyoto. The whole village is involved in the business in some way. People do everything from making paper to packaging stationery, binding blank books, printmaking, etc., there. Their work is marketed world wide.

Our other trip was to the home of the Fukunishi family who have been making Uda Washi - scroll backing paper - for 400 years. At the Fukunishi Studio we were allowed to use their equipment and actually make paper with them. It was an incredible experience!

Not only did the Fukunishi family open their home to us but the women of the family prepared us a wonderful lunch. We spent the night at a traditional county inn called Mayasuya Ryokan. After a community bath - we did separate by sexes - we were served an elaborate traditional meal. Our accommodations were complete with futons and rice hull pillows. Breakfast was egg drop soup with whole little fishes in it.

Highlights from the Symposium

During the International Paper Symposium, speakers from all over the world talked about and showed slides of their work. There was an exhibit of paper art and hands-on workshops in some of the traditional paper crafts of Japan. We also had lectures on the history of papermaking as well as its future. I have to admit while I was there I bought an incredible amount of paper! I hope to attend the IPS in Alice Springs, Australia in 1998.

Three years ago I went to the International Marbler's Gathering in San Francisco. While there I found a book on Japanese paper dolls and how to make them. Now I make miniature dolls as pins and I also do larger dolls, 6 to 12 inches tall. I really have been interested in Japanese arts and crafts since I was nine years old and saw an exhibit at the Detroit Art Institute and bought my first origami book.

~~~~~~~~~~~~~

Other Activities

Rajeania exhibits and sells her work at about two shows each year. Her work is sold in two galleries in Knoxville, Tennessee and at another in Dallas, Texas.

She teaches non-credit courses at the University of Tennessee in Knoxville, at the John C. Campbell Folk School in Brasstown, North Carolina, and does artist residencies in public schools for the Tennessee State Arts Commission.

Pictures of her kudzu paper are on the next page.
~~~~~~~~~~~~~

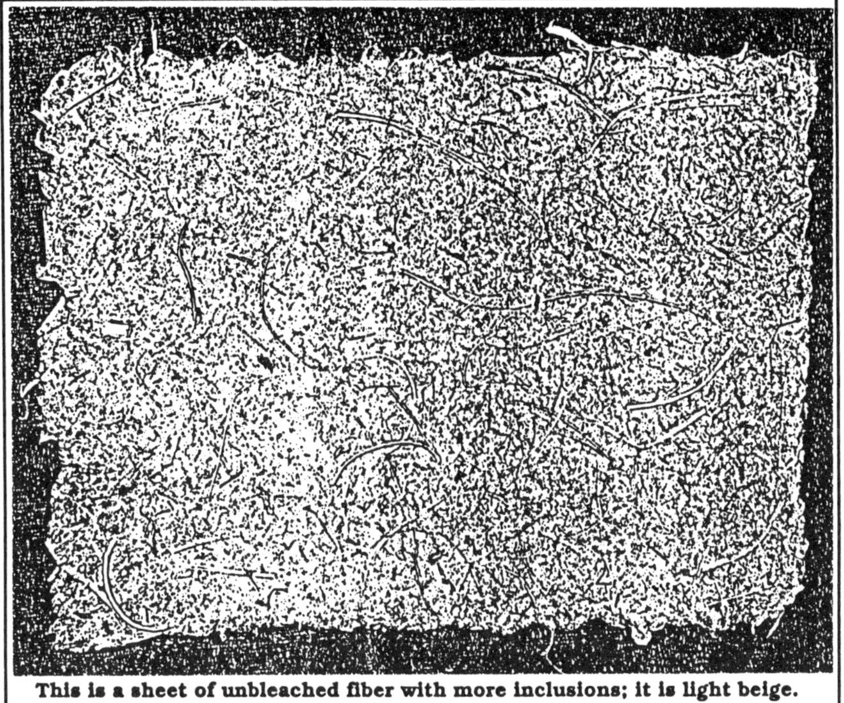

This is a sheet of unbleached fiber with more inclusions; it is light beige.

KUDZU PAPERS

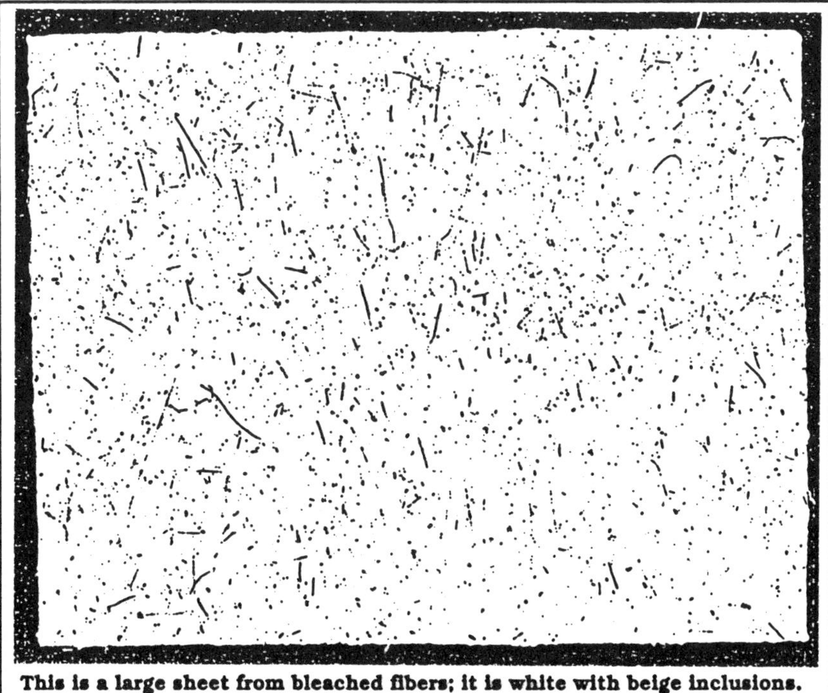

This is a large sheet from bleached fibers; it is white with beige inclusions.

KUDZU KLASS

Kudzu vines grow into a thick, tangled mass. In summer the leaves cover the vines so completely that it is impossible to see the ground underneath the growth. From the air, a large kudzu patch looks like a lake!

Aerial map makers would have less trouble if kudzu owners would take bulldozers and shove out the Chinese symbol for kudzu in the middle of the patch. It might inspire the phantoms who cut mysterious patterns in wheat fields to switch to kudzu patches. Here is the symbol if you want to try it.

This symbol is read as the word 'kuzu' in Japan, as 'ko' in China.

Chapter 11
Environmental Artist, Carol Stangler

Carol Stangler is an environmental educator and artist. She weaves baskets and sculptures from vines such as kudzu, bamboo, reed, bark, and other natural materials. Her work is exhibited in juried and invitational shows throughout the state of Georgia.

Carol has combined her love of nature and her sewing expertise into many art forms. She was named one of the five top style makers in Atlanta for 1995.

She has worked extensively as an environmental educator, putting her academic into practice as an artist in residence in many counties throughout Georgia. She has a Bachelor of Arts degree from American University, Washington, D. C., and a Master of Arts in Education from Georgia State University in Atlanta.

Here, in Carol's own words, is how one work of her artistic creations came to be.

My Harbinger of Change

When I began weaving baskets of native Georgia materials in 1981, kudzu was not my vine of choice. I considered its grey-brown color drab, its knobby texture reptilian. I much preferred wild grape, honeysuckle and wisteria. But after several years of trying to make a living weaving vine baskets, I yearned to create a new art form that wasn't as labor-intensive.

One night I had one of recurring snake dreams, this time with many snakes writhing and wrapping around one another. The next day, gathering in the kudzu fields, I saw, as though for the first time, kudzu's intricate twists spiralling up and around branches and vines.

I put two and two together and started experimenting with "Kudzu Snakes." I began timidly by painting the snakes realistic shades of greys and browns. It wasn't long, however, before I broke through into outlandish colors and fanciful patterns.

Now, after years of "handling" my kudzu snakes, my snake dreams are no longer fearful. Instead, the snakes come to me as my ally - protector and harbinger of change.

Carol Stangler and one of her "Kudzu Snakes" at the first Kudzu Art Show in Cochran, Georgia

Chapter 12
Kudzu Weaving Artist, Rosa Lee Thomas

Rosa Lee Thomas of Perry, Georgia achieved success as a kudzu weaving artist because she was resourceful. In 1984, she wanted to make baskets with oak but it was not available. Rather than abandon basket making, she taught herself to weave with kudzu, wisteria and grapevines.

Rosa Lee Thomas weaving a kudzu basket

In addition to baskets, she experimented and developed designs for kudzu roses and sunflowers.

Rosa's work came to public attention and today she is a 'true' folk artist. Her work has been shown at many places, including the Georgia Living Center in Perry, Georgia, and many other local shows. It was also in the kudzu exhibit entitled *The Art of Kudzu* at the Schiele Museum in Gastonia, North Carolina in 1995.

When one learns that in addition to her art work Rosa is the mother of twelve children, there is one very obvious conclusion: Rosa Lee Thomas was attracted to kudzu, the super vine of the South, because she is a Super Woman!

Rosa Lee Thomas holding one of her floral creations

Chapter 13
Kudzu Cuisine at Sky Valley, Janie Sue Yearwood, Chef

Janie Sue Yearwood encountered kudzu in fine cuisine in 1989, just six years before her death in 1995. The encounter occurred at Lake Allatoona at an 'Incredible Edibles' gathering of adventurous gourmets. She had been teaching the art of using kudzu to make baskets and other decorative items but eating it had never crossed her mind.

Very quietly, Janie took delicate nibbles of almost two dozen kudzu delectables - from kudzu-batter-fried chicken to kudzu-spiked lemonade. To her astonishment, she liked them all.

Within months, kudzu was the center of attention at Sky Valley Resort, in Northeast Georgia where she worked as a chef. She incorporated kudzu into everything from cocktails to casseroles. In 1990 she hosted the first Kudzu Festival at Sky Valley.

Later, her Kudzu-Cook-Offs became the event for unique dining and fun.

Janie left us with the benefit of her extensive of kudzu leaves. Here are some of her recommendations.

Kudzu leaves should be gathered when they are young and tender. Unless you get these, kudzu is tough. Gather in a place that has no curled, dead leaves. This condition may indicate herbicides or pesticides have been sprayed on it and could prove dangerous to anyone eating it.

Kudzu tastes similar to kale or mustard greens. It can be used almost as you would use either of these or any other

other green leafy vegetable. Use your imagination in addition to the ideas suggested here.

Add kudzu to most any vegetable casserole, toss a few chopped leaves into a basic corn bread recipe, or a Mexican corn bread recipe. It adds color, texture and an intriguing taste.

If you want the kudzu leaves extra tender, parboil them before adding to the other ingredients in the recipe.

Add chopped kudzu leaves to any quiche.

Cook kudzu leaves with your turnip greens and also with your turnips.

Kudzu leaves and stems can be crushed and added to your favorite cocktail. Submerge partially into the drink so it will flavor it much as a twist of lemon does.

The leaves are low in sodium and high in fiber and vitamins A, C and D.

Use kudzu powder to add flavor and thickening to sweet-and-sour sauces, apple pie and friend eggplant.

Kudzu leaves are a novelty item but should not be. There is a plentiful supply. My advice is to try it as a new food - you'll like it.

Janie loved kudzu vines as an art and craft material. After discovering it as a fine food, she loved the whole plant and proclaimed herself 'Kudzu Queen of North Georgia.'

Chapter 14
Kudzu Blossom Jelly
By: Diane Hoots

Kudzu blossom jelly is a gourmet delicacy which is sold in speciality shops. It is expensive because it is made from kudzu flowers which must be hand picked in hard to get at locations. You can, however, make your own.

The taste is distinctive, quite mild and pleasant. If the jelly is made from fresh blossoms, it will be light burgundy to purple in color. If the blossoms are frozen, the jelly might be golden.

Kudzu produces a beautiful purple flowers. In Georgia the blooming is from early summer to late fall. The blooming will vary from one geographical location to another. They are generally hidden from view under the dense cover of leaves, or on vines growing on top of trees were the tree leaves also hide them. Bees, especially bumblebees, love the flowers and are quick to defend their turf against intruders, especially late in the day. They are less aggressive in the mornings.

Harvesting Blossoms from the Flowers

Locate a growth of kudzu that you can ascertain has not been sprayed with either herbicides or pesticides. Also, the kudzu should not be growing next to major highways where it is subjected to automobile exhaust pollution. Since kudzu is so abundant, these criteria are not difficult.

Most property owners are incredulous but delighted to have persons harvest flowers and any other part of their kudzu patch. Small animals such as frogs, lizards, snakes and ground hogs live in most kudzu patches. There are also lots of insects and spiders, so be aware. Dress appropriately and exercise caution at all times while you are in the kudzu patch.

Harvesting kudzu flowers is hard work. Most grow low to the ground, among the mass of vines and under the leaves. Heat is also a problem so be sure to take proper precautions to deal with it.

Pick only fresh blossoms; do not gather old, browned ones. Fully opened blossoms are easy to pull from the flower stem. Wash harvested blossoms thoroughly.

Kudzu Blossom Jelly

4 cups kudzu blossoms
4 cups boiling water
1 tbsp lemon juice
1 package pectin
5 cups sugar

= Put washed blossoms in bowl

= Pour boiling water over blossoms, stir and set in refrigerator for 6 hours or overnight

= Strain and put liquid in medium pot (liquid will be brown but will turn burgundy when lemon is added

= Add lemon juice and pectin

= (Liquid may be frozen with lemon juice for future use.)

= Bring to a full rolling boil

= Add sugar, then bring to a second rolling boil, stirring constantly

= Allow to boil 2 minutes

= Skim foam, then pour into sterilized jars and seal

= Process jelly in boiling water bath canner for 5 minutes

Jelly should be made one batch (the quantity in this recipe) at a time; doubling it does not produce good jelly.

If something goes amiss and your jelly does not thicken properly, you have a delicious syrup!

My company, Krazy Kudzu Products, LTD. markets Kudzu Blossom Jelly. In 1994, I competed, and won a spot on the QVC shopping channel to sell my kudzu gift baskets.

I appeared on QVC on February 12, 1994. Kudzu Blossom Jelly and Syrup were tremendous hits with the viewers and demand for both, but especially the jelly, has increased since this exposure on national television.

Diane Hoots picking kudzu blossoms for her Kudzu Blossom Jelly and Kudzu Blossom Syrup

Dear Mrs. Hoots

Thank you for the jelly. and showing us some bastits and Some Wreaths and the Baer was sow cute. I liked all of It. Thank you for coming to show us that. Thank you It was fun

Love
Crystal

Crystal Malone wrote this thank-you note to Diane Hoots in November 1994 after a Kudzu demonstration at Shirley Hills Elementary School in Warner Robins, Georgia. Crystal was in the first grade.

Part III

Kudzu in Southern Culture

Chapter 15
Kudzu Art Exhibits

Diane Hoots of Warner Robins, Georgia organized the first Kudzu Art Exhibit in the United States. The exhibit was at Middle Georgia College in Cochran, Georgia, during March and April 1995.

The Kudzu Art Exhibit was so successful that Schiele Museum in Gastonia, North Carolina hosted an exhibit from September to November 1995.

In the interim between the exhibits at Cochran and Gastonia, six of the kudzu artists were invited to the Lofty Branch Gallery in Lakemont, Georgia for the month of July 1995 as part of its presentation: Kudzu Art. Regina Hines, Diane Hoots, Rosa Lee Thomas, Nancy Basket, Carol Stangler, Matthew Hoots and Pat Stark participated.

Kudzu as art is, to many Southerners, an idea whose time has not come. But for the dedicated group of very talented artists who turn kudzu into beautiful, interesting art, and useful items, the time for the idea came years ago. These artists have exhibited and sold their creations for years. The Kudzu Art Exhibit was the first opportunity to exhibit their work collectively.

Middle Georgia College Exhibit

Hal Lunsford at Middle Georgia College invited Diane Hoots to exhibit her kudzu art at the College. Diane's request to invite other artists and persons working with kudzu was granted. Exhibitors ranged in age from eight to advanced adulthood.

A part of the First Kudzu Art Show

Exhibitors and Items Exhibited

Nancy Basket and her daughter Joleen Oh, 12,: kudzu paper, pictures and baskets

William Bosshard, 11, basket

Richard Chatterton, basket, photography

Gayle Chatterton, dreamcatcher and godseye

Marcus Chatterton, 17, basket

Ryan Chatterton, 8, basket

Santiago, Cogollos, an exchange student from Spain, 18, basket

Diane Guillot, basket

Nicole Guillot, basket

Paula Hall, basket

Regina Hines, decorated baskets, wreaths, birdhouse, cornucopia and kudzu encircle mirrors

Marshall Hoots, basket made when he was age 5

Matthew Hoots, 9, baskets, teddy bears
Diane Hoots, baskets, photography, kudzupillers
Donna Licata, 3 baskets
Chris Lewallen, folk art, painted kudzu snake
Sheliva Neal, earrings made from Nancy Basket's kudzu paper, decorated with small wreaths
Kelli O'Neal, 13, basket
Shad O'Neal, 10, basket
Carol Stangler, painted kudzu snakes
Pat Stark, basket
Valerie Stark, basket
Ann Walls, basket

Rosa Lee Thomas did not exhibit her work but displayed baskets, kudzu sunflowers and roses for sale.

Schiele Museum Exhibit

The Art of Kudzu exhibit was hosted in the largest changing exhibit room at Schiele Museum which is used for parties and receptions. Persons attending functions which were held there while The Art of Kudzu exhibit was there told others about it. This word of mouth coverage made the show successful despite limited media coverage.

Exhibitors in The Art of Kudzu show were: Nancy Basket, Richard, Gayle, Ryan and Marcus Chatterton, Regina Hines, Marshall, Matthew and Diane Hoots, Carol Stangler Pat Stark and Rosa Lee Thomas.

Public Response

Despite the expected incredulous skepticism that kudzu and art could be on the same planet, the overwhelming response was very positive. The predominant theme in attendees' comments was amazement that kudzu is a very versatile art material. The second theme was a tongue-in-cheek relief that a way had been found to stop kudzu from growing!

Kudzu art exhibits have become more frequent as more artists work with kudzu and the public demand for the work they produce continues to increase.

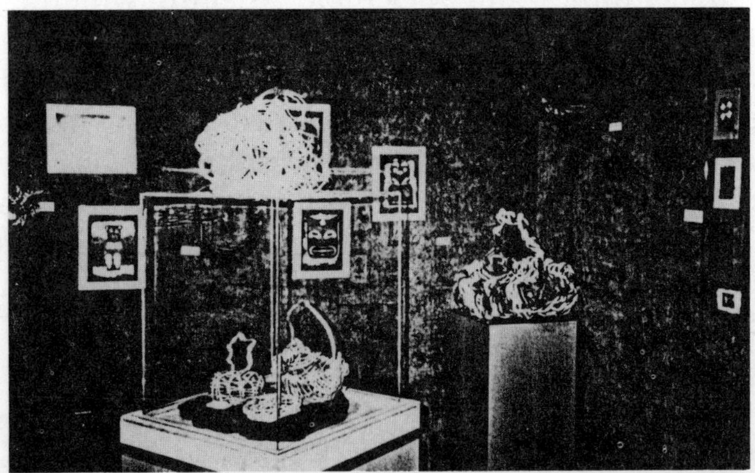

Photos made at The Art of Kudzu Exhibit at Schiele Museum, Gastonia, North Carolina, in 1995

Chapter 16
Kudzu Festivals and Kudzu Balls

Kudzu Festivals and Kudzu Balls are Southern creations. Why a festival, or ball, to celebrate the vine holding the record for less than flattering nicknames? "Why not?" ask festival organizers. It's a way to turn frustration into fun. You celebrate what you have - cherry blossoms, apples, ice. We have kudzu.

Publicists for kudzu festivals use words which tell us that they are a celebration of the amazing, blooming oriental legume. Translation: a party with a kudzu motif, complete with food, music, games and fun, generally to benefit a charity or cultural endeavor.

Between the 1940s and 1980s, several towns and cities held kudzu balls. In the late 1980s, in Chattanooga, Tennessee, what began as a joke among some friends led to a long running fund raiser for the Chattanooga Birth Defects Center. They called themselves the Long-Range, Way-Down-The-Road and Out-Of-Sight Planning Commission. They staged a Kudzu Costume Ball where partygoers could wash down a hot dog, including slaw and relish, with a green liquid purported to be kudzu squeezings wine cooler, all for $2.00! Their ball parodied the Cotton Ball where a debutante's father had to pay a $450.00 presentation fee. The organizers of the Cotton Ball claimed no malice toward the Kudzu organizers.

At the time this book went to press, we could find no scheduled Kudzu Balls but several Kudzu Festivals are scheduled for 1996. Those we know about are listed on the last page of this Chapter, in the last paragraph. They are also listed in Appendix A under Kudzu Activities. For the readers who have never been to a kudzu festival, this is an overview of staple and unique events condensed from about one hundred festival programs.

Arts and Crafts

Kudzu items generally displayed, or made during the festival, include baskets, paper and wreaths. Many other arts and crafts that do not use kudzu as a material but decorate with it are shown. Among these are pottery and fabric creations, stained glass, oil paintings, watercolors, quilts, tee shirts and all styles of hats.

At some festivals hats are decorated with live kudzu vines and leaves are featured, along with live kudzu crowns. Getting kudzu for festivals is normally not a problem. City departments cut it by the truckload and

Music and Literature

Many festivals stage contests in advance of the festival date offering prizes for the best music, poem, or short story about kudzu. Winning entries are presented at the festival.

In Knoxville, Tennessee a Kudzu Chorus sang a winning entry *Forever the Battle of Kudzu* to the tune of *The Battle Hymn of the Republic.* The first verse is:

"My eyes have seen kudzu, as it creeps across the grass
It climbs up every light pole, it attacks the home in mass.
It fills up every hillside and it creeps up every tree
It's marching on you see."

Most poems and stories are tongue-in-cheek. Titles that

have won are: *My Love for You Grows Like Kudzu, Were You There When the Frost Killed the Kudzu, That Embraceable Vine, and Beautiful Botanical Beast.*

Dance

Kudzu festivals are an opportunity for local dance school students and regional folk dancers to perform. The dancers adorn their costumes with live kudzu. Others are imprinted with leaves, flower and seed pods and even roots.

In one dance routine all the dancers wore costumes approximating kudzu vines. They brought down the house with their rendition of kudzu growing to the tune of *"Tell Me Why the Ivy Twines."*

While the dancers were entwined as a kudzu patch, two other dancers appeared on stage. One was tagged 'Ms. Poison Ivy,' and the other 'Mr. Kudzu.' Ms. Ivy told Mr. Kudzu that she had heard humans talking the other day that the world would end if poison ivy ever married kudzu, then asked, "Are you ready?" Mr. Kudzu fled from the stage.

Food

Kudzu is a food featured at kudzu festivals. It is offered in many forms for the adventurous. For the less adventurous, the old favorites - hot dogs, hamburgers, soft drinks, cotton candy and popcorn are there.

Deep fried or stir fried kudzu, kudzu pasta and tea are featured most often. For those who may never to get a kudzu festival but may wish to try these unusual dishes, here are two recipes.

Deep Fried Kudzu

Pick kudzu leaves no more than 3" in diameter from a

patch that is away from areas that may have been sprayed with herbicides or pesticides. Wash thoroughly and dry on paper towels before frying.

Make a batter of: 1 cup flour
1 beaten egg
3/4 cup any type sweet milk
salt and pepper

Heat : 1 cup oil in skillet until a drop of batter browns quickly

Dip each leaf into the batter and drop into the oil; fry until the crust is golden brown. Drain on paper towels and serve warm.

Stir Fried Kudzu

Wash and drain: 4 cups fresh, green kudzu leaves

Dice: 1 small onion and the kudzu leaves if desired

Heat: 2 tablespoons of oil in a large, skillet or wok. Test with a kudzu leaf. When it sizzles and wilts immediately, drop the kudzu leaves and the onion into the skillet and stir constantly until tender. Season to taste with soy sauce or salt and pepper.

A reporterer covering a kudzu festival asked two women if they were going to try the deep fried kudzu leaves.

One replied, "I tried a leaf and it tasted a bit like cardboard."

The other woman smiled and said, "I agree but my husband is over there ordering his third helping."

"He liked it that much?" the reporter asked skeptically.

"Who knows?" she replied candidly. "He refused to taste it until he overheard the man who is frying it confide to a customer that kudzu is a dandy aphrodisiac!"

Walks and Races

Several towns include charity walks and races in the

begin and/or end at the festival site so festival attendees are motivated to stay and enjoy the activities until the participants return.

Birmingham, Alabama has a 3.1 mile Kudzu Run annually to benefit charity. Runners are charged an entry fee. Trophies are presented to the first, second and third place winners in each category in the Run.

The rest of the day is spent in free activities for adults and children, including fun-filled singing displays.

How to Get Information About Kudzu Festivals

Write or call the Bureau of Tourism in any state south of Kentucky and west to Texas. Also check on the Internet.

Travel agents, especially those who arrange group tours, will have the information or can get it for you.

Kudzu festivals are an annual event in many towns, but most are not.

Holly Springs, Mississippi, Birmingham, Alabama and Providence Canyon in Georgia have had an annual festival in August for many years and all have festivals planned for 1996.

Kudzu Klass

KUDZU VINE

7240

KUDZU VINE
(Pueraria Thunbergiana)

PERENNIAL CLIMBER HEIGHT 20 TO 30 FEET

A rapid growing and vigorous vine with large heart-shaped leaves. Produces a profusion of small, purple pea-shaped blossoms late in the season, in sections where Winters are mild and vine does not die down to the ground. Ideal for covering arbors and trellises, and for screening porches.

PLANTING DIRECTIONS

WHERE AND WHEN TO PLANT: Plant seed outdoors in a sunny location after all danger of frost is past, or indoors in pots for setting out later.

HOW TO PLANT: Cover seed ¼ inch with fine soil, well pressed down.

HOW TO THIN OR TRANSPLANT: When plants are a few inches tall, thin or transplant to 4 inches apart. When vines are about 12 inches tall give them some support for climbing.

REMARKS: The seed coat is very hard so, to hasten germination, notch the seed or soak in water overnight.

PRICE 35 CENTS
STOCK NO. 7290
PACKED FOR 1972

No. 2160

Kudzu seeds: This is a Kudzu Vine seed package, priced at 35 cents in 1972, the year the Department of Agriculture declared kudzu a weed. Despite this declaration, suppliers have sold kudzu seeds sporadically since then. We checked many sources in June 1996 but found no suppliers in the United States. Seeds may be harvested from vertically-growing vines in late summer or early fall after they are fully mature. The pods will be dark brown.

Chapter 17
Kudzu Exhibit at the Museum of the New South

The kudzu plant, having achieved near mythic status in the history of the New South, was an important inclusion in the introductory exhibit at the Museum of the New South in Charlotte, North Carolina. The "New South A to Z" exhibit highlighted the blend of tradition and change that mold the New South era. Letters of the alphabet were used to guide visitors as they explored the forces that have shaped life in Charlotte and the Carolina Piedmont region since 1877.

The letter "K", of course, stands for kudzu. While the exhibit was open January - August 1996, visitors stuck paper kudzu leaves on the wall. By June, the wall was virtually covered.

Kudzu has its ardent Southern supporters despite the fact that many others consider it a pesky weed. Its supporters use it to make everything from jelly, syrup and candy to baskets, cloth and paper.

Kudzu is venerated in music and poetry, celebrated in countless festivals and immortalized in Doug Marlette's comic strip *Kudzu*. This legendary vine has found its way into Southern culture much as it has invaded the region's landscape.

The Museum of the New South is intent on preserving the history of Charlotte and the Carolina Piedmont as change and development continues. Like the kudzu plant, the Charlotte area keeps growing and growing and growing! The Museum's focus is on the period after the Civil War and Reconstruction when Charlotte became known as a modern city. It sees itself as the community memory that encourages people to be sensitive to the past in order to understand the present and prepare for the future.

Chapter 18
Kudzu - - - Kudzoo, Baby Gorilla at Zoo Atlanta

There was great excitement throughout Atlanta when a baby gorilla was born on February 8, 1994 to Choomba and Willie B. at Zoo Atlanta. The sex of the baby could not immediately be determined but everybody was invited to enter a "Name Baby B." contest to choose its name. There were 63,424 entries. The winning name -- *KUDZU* -- was submitted by Paul Polenski of Duluth.

On August 1, 1994, Zoo Atlanta announced that baby gorilla, Kudzu, was a girl. Kudzu, it was reported, was growing "like a weed" and visitors were invited to see her toddling around within a few steps of her mother, Choomba. Kudzu and Choomba were residing with daddy Willie B. and two other gorillas.

You were put on alert at the beginning of this book that kudzu triggers a spelling malfunction in many folks. Apparently this malfunction was triggered at Zoo Atlanta. Baby *Kudzu* became Baby *Kudzoo.*

Baby Kudzoo's Parents

Baby Kudzoo was the second baby born to mother Choomba, and was father Willie B.'s first offspring. She was the sixth gorilla baby born at Zoo Atlanta.

Willie B. was successfully socialized with other gorillas in 1989, after living alone for 27 years. Only a year earlier, he had his first chance to experience a natural, outdoor habitat, when a donation by the Ford Motor Company and the loan of three groups of gorillas from the Yerkes Primate Research Center made possible the opening of the Ford African Rain Forest at Zoo Atlanta.

Choomba was introduced into Willie B.'s group in the Ford African Rain Forest in October 1992. They produced Kudzoo. Zoo Atlanta anticipates that she will help perpetuate the gorilla population, an endangered species.

Kudzoo the baby gorilla stays close to her mommy Choomba as she explores the Ford African Rain Forest at Zoo Atlanta. Kudzoo was named in a public contest which drew tens of thousands of votes from the Atlanta community. (Photo by SEBO)

Chapter 19
A Kudzu Anthology

Kudzu has inspired millions of lines. Here are some of them.

A Contribution to the Empty Stocking Fund

Each year, just before Christmas, someone sends a contribution to The Knoxville News-Sentinel Empty Stocking Fund. The contributor's signature is "The Kudzu Garden Club."

~ ~ ~

Get a machete, Maggie! Here it comes again!

This is one of Doug Marlette's first episodes in his comic strip *KUDZU;* it is printed with his permission.

My Fetish: *KUDZU*
By: Bebe Cook

I have reason to believe that kudzu became my fetish when I was about two years old. My parents often told me that when we would ride from Thomaston to Macon, here in Georgia, to visit my grandparents, I would stand in the car, point at all the kudzu along the way and yell, "Look, look, look!" My fascination with the lush green vine has only grown stronger as I have grown older.

Once, when I was hospitalized for surgery, the secretary at the school where I taught presented me with a big, beautiful vase of kudzu. Bless her heart, she had been subjected to the stares of passers-by along the road as she harvested her bouquet, not to mention the incredulous sidelong glances of her fellow passengers on the hospital elevator! During that hospital stay, I received many outstanding floral arrangements but none so lovely as the kudzu.

My mother was quite embarrassed some years ago when she brought a visitor to my apartment. I had a bowl of kudzu gracing the coffee table. The guest - a frequent judge at flower shows - remarked that the bowl of greenery looked very similar to common kudzu. My mother mumbled that it was 'somewhat similar,' giving me a glance which said I was not to volunteer any information. The visitor pronounced the display beautiful!

On my fortieth birthday, a special friend gave me an enormous hanging basket of kudzu. Well, as you can imagine, the vine grew and grew until it broke the pot, spilling the prolific vine out all over my front porch. Later, some of my friends confided that they feared the neighbors would want to have me evicted!

For several summers I had the pleasure of teaching gifted second, third and fourth graders at Mercer University in Macon, Georgia. I was allowed to write my own courses, and wrote curriculum for four courses. The most popular by far was *Rapunzel, the Titanic and Kudzu - A Creative Approach to Learning.* Making and *eating* kudzu salad was a delight for the children and the highlight of the course. We even served it to some friends who visited our class from the local Board of Education.

As an elementary curriculum director for Bibb County, Georgia, I had the opportunity to conduct many kudzu workshops for children. These were always as much fun for me as the students.

Before I retired, one of the elementary schools in my district honored me with a program at which I was crowned Queen of Kudzu for the Middle Georgia area. I was presented with a Kudzu Crown, a Kudzu Scepter, and a royal robe. Needless to say, it was a joyous occasion.

Now that I am retired, I have numerous opportunities as a professional storyteller to share my love of kudzu with others. I enjoy no greater pleasure.

I know not why, but Kudzu is mine!
Long live the Kudzu Vine!

Written May 7, 1996 in Macon, Georgia. Bebe Cook is Elizabeth Baker Cook, an educator, storyteller and adventurer. Friends describe her as a deeply religious woman who keeps a prayer journal. Bebe contracted polio in 1956 which left her with a permanent limp but she does not let that get in the way of hopping on a hot air balloon or riding her motorized ski on Lake Tobesofkee in Georgia, where she lives.

The Ballad Of Henry Lee

By Al King

Henry Lee was driving hard
Down a lonely country road.
His head was working overtime
On an extra heavy load.

The wind outside his pickup truck
Was whipping up a storm.
The lightning shot big thunderbolts
At every moving form.

He heard the first few thumpitty-thumps
But didn't pay a mind
To what was going on back there,
And didn't look behind.

Then all at once he felt a funny
Grabbing from the rear.
It happened several times
And forced him to a lower gear.

The lightning made the sky like day
Just long enough for him
To see a terrifying sight
Before the night went dim.

A kudzu patch had gotten loose
And headed 'cross the road
In search of something else to climb
Before it all got mowed.

It curled around a crosstie
He was hauling in the back,
Then got inside the cab with him
By crawling through a crack.

The creeping thing came at him
As he shoved her into low,
And gave her all the gas he could
To make the old truck go.

But nothing had a chance against
A kudzu patch gone wild.
It grabbed his bumpers front and back
And then got really riled.

It stood up in the road ahead
And waited for him there,
Then twined around his wheels and doors
And thrashed out at the air.

His hands released the steering wheel
And caught a piece of vine
As it came twisting 'round his neck
From somewhere off behind.

He let out with an awful scream
And struggled in the night;
But soon the fight was over,
And everything got quiet.

The thunder stopped its clapping.
The wind grew strangely calm.
The moon came out and healed the night
With soothing rays of balm.

And Henry rested easy,
The way the dead all do.
He didn't give another thought
To earthly cares—or kudzu.

They found him in November
After Jack Frost paid his call.
The leaves turned brown and withered
As they do late in the fall.

And opened up the gulley
To the eyes of passers-by,
Who saw the truck uncovered
For the first time since July.

And all made speculation
As to what had caused his death—
A heart attack, or liquor,
Which was sometimes on his breath;

But no one could have guessed the truth
Because they didn't see
The kudzu patch that crossed the road
And lassoed Henry Lee.

Al King of Rt. 5, Rutherfordton, says he wrote The Ballad of Henry Lee after driving along a South Carolina highway where kudzu was so thick "it was like a jungle."

Since then, he's recited the poem at a number of public programs—and now has it set to music.

King, who is assistant to the president and director of quality control at Stonecutter Mills in Spindale, has been an amateur country music songwriter for the past 10 years. A native of Rutherford County, he is a member of Rutherford Electric Membership Corporation, Forest City.

This Ballad is printed with permission of Mrs. Al King of Rutherfordton, North Carolina. We appreciate her contribution.

A Letter about Kudzu

June 19, 1996

Dear Mrs. Hoots,

My name is Michelle Baker. I am in the eleventh grade at Eagles Landing High School in Stockbridge, Georgia. I did a project which I titled "Kudzu: Does it Serve a Purpose." My grade on it was 100!

I researched and wrote a paper, made a backboard, a kudzu vine basket, and kudzu candy. My conclusion is: yes, nutrient rich bacteria help the soil. I am sending you some photos of me with my project materials.

Michelle Baker

Part IV

Making the Best

of the Kudzu Predicament

Part IV

Chapter 20 Calhoun County, Georgia Kudzu Creative Product Competition

In October 1993, the Economic Development Committee of Calhoun County, Georgia created a "Kudzu Creative Product Competition." The purpose of the Competition was to find someone with a new idea for something that could be mass produced from kudzu and create jobs.

The Committee announced the Competition in this news release:

"Greenfield Plantation
Morgan, Georgia 31766
News Release
Kudzu - Pest or Asset?
Calhoun County Development Commission will pay for solutions

The kudzu vine, which grows all over the southeast, has become a real pest. Brought over from Japan in 1876, it was a harmless ornamental plant. But in the 1930s, the Department of Agriculture (USDA) discovered it had an extensive root system. Kudzu would hold the soil together on eroded farms; and these farms were plentiful in the depression era.

So the USDA had kudzu planted with abandon. In time these vines grew prolifically, and today in many areas they have taken over the countryside. Landowners have found kudzu to be difficult and expensive to eliminate.

Now Calhoun County through its Economic Development Committee (CCEDC) believes it has the answer which will benefit the entire southeast. On October 16th in Morgan, the CCEDE will sponsor a "Kudzu Creative Product Competition" (KCPC). The purpose of this competition is to seek a product made of kudzu which is so useful that there will be a need for it and therefore it will lend itself to mass production.

Once this product has been created there would be virtually limitless raw materials for it, available simply for the asking. To harvest a landowner's kudzu would do him a favor. This Kudzu Creative Product Competition will transform a vine that is now a pest to a vine which would be inventory for a new industry giving many jobs for Calhoun and all rural counties.

Calhoun County wants to attract industry so our children have work here when they leave school and won't have to leave the county. Prize money is presently being collected and further competition information is obtainable from the address above."

~~~~~~~~~~

E. D. Dunn, Jr. was the primary spokesman for the Kudzu Creative Product Competition. "We've got to do something in this county to get industry," he said. "We're not interested in arts and crafts. We have nothing against arts and crafts but we want something - we don't know what it is - that can be mass produced and put a lot of people to work. We've got to take advantage of what we've got and create jobs for our young people so they won't have to move away. We're hoping there's gold in those pesky green vines."

The primary industry in Calhoun County is farming. The largest employers are government and the school system. Rocked by plant closings the county needed industrial stability in 1993, and the situtation has not changed.
~~~~~~~~~~

While the land covered by kudzu in Calhoun County grows by leaps and bounds each year, the human population has dwindled. Since 1940, the county's population has dropped from 10,000 to 5,000.

In commenting on the competition, kudzu expert Jake Tinga, a retired horticulture instructor from the University of Georgia said Calhoun County may be on to something. If it does not work the first time, perhaps it should be tried again and also tried in other areas. Kudzu has such a bad reputation, people hesitate to say anything good about it but this is a grand way to look for new ideas.

Mr. Dunn saw kudzu devour a tract of his pine trees in the early 1950s when he moved to Georgia from New York. "Kudzu has been more or less in my hair ever since," he said, "so we must try to do something about it."

Competition Results

The Kudzu Creative Competition was held on October 16, 1993 as scheduled. The Committee was disappointed that there were only two entrants.

One entry was a process for deriving ethanol from kudzu and the other had developed a biodegradable planting pot made of kudzu leaves and twigs.

The Committee divided the $700 prize money evenly between the entrants.

Unfortunately neither process attracted a company to produce them in Calhoun.

~~~~~

Mr. Dunn said in a telephone interview during June 1996, that the competition had not been held again but he hopes it will be. He suggests that other areas with the resources to organize and publicize a kudzu competition should try it for the mutual benefit of all the South.
~~~~~

KUDZU KLASS

Legislation and the fight against kudzu: In February 1994, Georgia State Representative Tom Buck introduced legislation to make it a misdemeanor for a property owner to allow kudzu to grow onto adjoining property.

Introduction of the proposed legislation resulted from a complaint from a resident of Chattahoochee County whose property was under siege from kudzu. It was marching onto his property from the property that adjoined his for quite a distance. The owner of the property with the kudzu was taking no action to confine it within his own property lines.

Although much empathy for the afflicted recipient of unwanted kudzu was expressed, the legislation did not pass - that time.

Chapter 21
Kudzu as a Fuel Source

Dr. Robert Tanner, a chemical engineer, at Vanderbilt University in Nashville, Tennessee, has conducted research on kudzu as a renewable fuel, food and textile resource. The results were that kudzu is an excellent source for a commercial outlet for each of these uses.

Fuel for Gasoline Engines

Despite the news spots that a way has been found to turn kudzu into fuel for gasoline engines, we are not there yet. As of June 1996, no process has been found to produce a 100% kudzu fuel for gasoline engines.

Most of the media spots were probably written to grab reader/listener attention and they got mine. I have been tempted to stick a kudzu vine in my gas tank and let it grow fuel as I drive along but I probably would not get very far.

Ethanol, which is also called ethyl alcohol, can be distilled from kudzu. Kudzu ethanol could be combined with unleaded gasoline and the result would be a very satisfactory fuel for gasoline engines. Many suppliers sell this type fuel under the trade name gasohol. Gasohol is a mixture of approximately 90% unleaded petroleum gasoline and 10% ethanol. But, as yet, no supplier sells gasohol that is a combination of petroleum gasoline and kudzu ethanol.

In Dr. Tanner's work, kudzu root starch was test for suitability for production of enthanol and lysine-enriched baker's yeast.

The biggest drawback to kudzu ethanol is that the harvesting and processing methodologies have not been developed to make it commercially profitable.

One new method of harvesting the kudzu root starch, in sap form, was tested during Dr. Tanner's study and found feasible. While still in the ground, kudzu roots are injured but not divided and the sap was collected via tubes. The method is similar to harvesting maple sugar.

Collecting the sap from the living plant could provide a raw material for six months each year. The steps to process the sap into a marketable fuel component of gasohol or food source, such as baker's yeast, would be relatively simple. A plant could be build and workers trained quickly for a reasonable investment.

Dr. Tanner is continuing his research on kudzu. A summary of his current work on kudzu as a textile source is in the Kudzu Cloth Chapter of this book.

Methane Gas

Methane gas can be produced from kudzu. It can be used in items which use natural gas and to make methanol, which is a mixture of methane gas and ethanol/alcohol. Methanol is used as a fuel, in the manufacture of formaldehyde, smokeless powders and paints.

Dr. B. C. Wolverton of the National Space Technology Laboratories in Bay St. Louis in Mississippi found that one pound of dried kudzu can produce 4 to 5 cubic feet of methane gas.

Methane gas is produced by natural or artificially induced decomposition of vegetable matter. Kudzu was found to decompose readily and easily by a natural bacterial process.

Dr. Wolverton was so impressed by these findings that he thinks it within the realm of reason that the day could come when home owners could 'grow their own methane gas.'

A home owner would grow a row of kudzu near the house, harvest the vines and put them in a tank. Bacteria would digest the vines and form methane gas and carbon dioxide. The carbon dioxide would be siphoned out of the tank by an automatic device. The methane gas would be stored in a tank with a pipe connecting it to the house. Presto! Kudzu gas on demand.

Dr. Wolverton requested help from the Department of Energy to perfect this environmentally sound methane gas system for homes. No help has been forthcoming.

Reality Check

Development of Dr. Tanner's and Dr. Wolverton's proven uses of kudzu may just come from a future kudzu magnet reading this, not from our Government

KUDZU KLASS

Angora goats and kudzu: Dr. Errol G. Rhoden of Tuskegee University reports that researchers there are utilizing fields of kudzu to raise Angora goats.

Three benefits accrue to Tuskegee from this endeavor. First, it helps ecology because they are using land that would otherwise be considered wasteland. Second, the goats produce a very nutritious milk. Third, the goats produce an excellent quality of wool from which a variety of products can be made.

The kudzu provides a continuing food source for the goats because they are rotated from area to area in the kudzu patch. If this is not done, Dr. Rhoden says, the constant grazing will eventually eradicate the kudzu.

~~~~~~~~~~

Kudzu used to dye wool: Nancy Roberson of Knoxville, Tennessee is a weaver. She makes a dye for dying wool from kudzu leaves. The color is a beautiful, almost translucent green.
~~~~~~~~~~

Chapter 22
Kudzu Farmers, Edith and W. Henry Edwards

While most of kudzu's friends today prefer silence to the possible ire of their neighbors, a few speak out. Despite the fact that the United States Department of Agriculture has downgraded kudzu to weed status, its loyal friends know it has many beneficial uses.

Edith and Henry Edwards found kudzu to be a friend when they needed a friend and they now befriend it at every opportunity.

They have one message about kudzu: it is a wonderful food source for humans and animals. If properly used, kudzu can become an important link in the food chain.

The Edwards practice what they preach about kudzu on their farm, Kudzu Konnection, in Rutherfordton, North Carolina. They also spread the kudzu message by radio and television appearances. Kudzu festivals are favorite pilgrimages where they share what they have learned and glean information from kindred souls. In 1982, Edith fried kudzu leaves at the World's Fair in Knoxville, Tennessee.

Edith conducts kudzu seminars for church groups and garden clubs and at Isothermal Community College in Polk County, North Carolina. They know the speaker has arrived when they see an automobile sporting a license plate: KUDZU. She shares the knowledge she has gained over the past fifteen years about the value of kudzu in the human diet. It is used very much like any other leafy vegetable but most persons prefer it cooked rather than raw in salads.

This is the Edwards' narrative of how they came to be in the rare and unique position of Kudzu Evangelists.

Kudzu: Manna in the Wilderness
By: Edith and W. Henry Edwards

Our family's journey to 'manna in the wilderness' for a dairy herd between 1962-1977 in western North Carolina taught us to look everywhere for growing/green forage. Several summers during this period, the regular forages for cattle were withered/dry due to lack of moisture. Wherever Kudzu (Pueraria lobata) abounded, it was green, lush and plentiful. Therefore, we asked authorities if kudzu was safe for cattle to eat.

A trip to Clemson University, in South Carolina, Dairy Department gave us the knowledge we needed to go forward in using kudzu for our herd. Not only did the cattle like kudzu - like bees going to honey - but the milk production was greater than ever. Our record has not been topped by other dairymen (from more milk given from cows, per day, per cow) from kudzu silage.

North Carolina State University, Raleigh, North Carolina, Dairy Department tested kudzu hay at the dry stage, after it was baled, and 21% protein was documented on this feed; higher in protein than alfalfa.

We purchased a Fox mower-chopper to be pulled by a tractor and 'green chopped' the kudzu which blew into a truck body. Then it was hauled to a ground silo, continuing until the silo was full. Someone was on a tractor packing (going back and forth) on the silage. It 'pickled' overnight!

For most other animals, especially horses, we cut, rake and bale the kudzu; using a square bale header. We cut twice each season, in July and October. Be sure when you go into a field with machinery there are no tree stumps, etc. for they will ruin a good cause. Set your header 'low' and cut vines low. Then when you go back to bale set the header 'high.' These two requirements are a must!!! If a round baler is available, the kudzu twines itself and does not require baling twine.

Baling kudzu hay at Kudzu Konnection, Rutherfordton, North Carolina

Kudzu covers about 10 acres of our 300 acre farm. Each year we produce about 1,000 bales of kudzu hay and sell it as feed for cattle and horses. It is very high quality and does not contain any known toxic compounds.

Green kudzu is well liked by livestock, including cattle, horses, sheep, hogs, goats, rabbits and poultry. In fact, animals like it so much they will tear down a fence to get to it.

Krafty-Kudzu

The Edwards think if Kudzu could speak, this would probably be what it would say:

My name is Krafty-Kudzu and I'm coming your way to enlighten everybody into the protein/fiber sway. If you happen to be in the locale where you can pick or pull me out, you'll discover I'm a versatile, miracle, mystery plant to never be without!

All of these words are meaningful for Kudzu, one of, if not the only one plant of its kind to have all parts of the plant utilized by man and beasts! A true message especially for those who are looking for more 'protein and fiber' in their food. How you say? Continue to read this story about how the farmer and his wife have grown in knowledge to dig, pick, pull, admire, appreciate, control and tell the world what Kudzu's all about!

Telling the World Through a Best Seller

Kudzu was in full bloom when Phyllis Whitney, the world-wide known mystery writer, came to the Chimney Rock/Lake Lure communities in North Carolina in the early 1990s. Mrs. Whitney asked the farmer's wife, Edith, about Kudzu. Edith told her it was time people stopped cursing kudzu and started realizing the needs it can meet for them.

Mrs. Whitney heard the message and wrote about it in her book *Star Flight*, released in 1993. Kudzu is mentioned 15 times in this story and the book is a world best seller! Thus, many more folks are learning about the potential of this plant called kudzu.

Kudzu on the Dining Table

Edith advises persons considering adding kudzu to their diet to read *The Book of Kudzu* by William Shurtleff and Akiko Aoyagi, husband and wife writers. The book was published in 1977 and Edith bought it in 1981 at the suggestion of a cousin. It lay on her kitchen counter for several months but once she opened it, it has stayed open.

We were delighted to find out so many ways to utilize kudzu. Recipes/directions are given which made us realize humans could also enjoy eating different parts of the plant.

In fact we were so thrilled with this treasure trove about kudzu that we called and spoke with the authors at their home in California. They were pleased to learn their book had been so well received and so helpful.

William Shurtleff said, "I really like people with a mission in life. These people have found a plant that they like and have decided to teach other people about its beneficial uses. I think that is wonderful."

Red Letter Day and Beyond

For this farmer's wife, Red Letter Day was August 22, 1981 when she first served French Fried Kudzu leaves to her husband. What a pleasurable surprise!

Since that day, she and her husband, have, and continue to share their knowledge of kudzu throughout the Southeastern United States where it is readily available.

Several years ago, Trinett Wellsley, one of Edith's students at a Kudzu Seminar, took the challenge to make kudzu cloth. Trinett followed the procedures in the *Book of Kudzu* for extracting fiber from the kudzu vines. The norm is that 52 pounds of kudzu vines are required to make one pound of fiber filament. Trinett used an old-fashioned hand loom to weave the kudzu into approximately three yards of cloth and made it into a vest for herself.

For several years we have shared our viewpoint on kudzu with many students of Professor Thomas Tucker at Isothermal College in Polk County, North Carolina. Professor Tucker gives his students a choice of writing a paper on Shakespeare or kudzu. Most choose kudzu and come to Kudzu Konnection as part of their research.

We are convinced there is much more to be discovered about kudzu.

The most recent sharing of knowledge was when this kudzu farmer and his wife appeared in a video made by The University of Alabama Center for Public Television and Radio, entitled *The Amazing Story of Kudzu.*

What next? Who knows? Krafty Kudzu is full of uses for those who like a challenge! And here we are, ready for the next Krafty Kudzu challenge.

Edith and W. Henry Edwards

Chapter 23
Kudzu Cloth

Despite an extensive search, we did not locate any weavers of kudzu cloth in the United States. If they are out there, we hope they will contact us and share their adventures in this unique use of kudzu.

Kudzu Fiber Research

Dr. Robert D. Tanner, and a group of researchers at Vanderbilt University in Nashville, Tennessee, investigated the use of kudzu fibers for use by the textile industry. The conclusion at the end of their investigative study was that kudzu plants can provide high quality fibrous materials to the textile industry.

Kudzu fibers were found to have a remarkable combination of properties: durability, strength, natural light yellow color and purity. These properties make kudzu fibers attractive and desirable. Natural fibers are obtained as ready yarn but of variable width, rather than individual fibers. These fibers can be spun easily into bulky yarns in any large scale textile production.

This fiber study was conducted on kudzu vines harvested in late fall, winter and spring, from the wild in Nashville, Tennessee and Muscle Shoals, Alabama. Kudzu fibers are extracted from the woody vines and are classified in the bast fiber category, i.e., fiber extracted from the interior part of the plant sheath.

The fibers were extracted by natural retting (the process of separating the woody part from the filamentous part of a plant). The vines were cut in lengths of approximately 6 inches each, and submerged in tap water at room temperature. Natural bacteria and fungi in the vines caused a fermentation and the sheath of the vine to degrade. The retting process is complete when the outer sheath of the vine can be removed easily under flowing tap water without mechanical assistance.

The core of fibrous material is removed from the sheath, separated and dried at room temperature.

Each group of vines was tested for tensile strength. The tensile strength of vines harvested in late fall, winter and spring varied. However, all were found to have sufficient tensile strength to compete with other natural fibers presently used in the textile industry.

~~~~~~~~~

The study was published in *Applied Biochemistry and Biotechnology*, Volume 57/58, Spring 1996, pages 75-89, under the title *The Effect of Fermentation (Retting) Time and Harvest Time on Kudzu (Pueraria lobata) Fiber Strength.*

~~~~~~~~~

Kudzu Grasscloth Wall Covering

The walls of thousands of American homes is decorated with grasscloth made mainly from kudzu. Most of this grasscloth, commonly marketed to as grasscloth wall covering is imported from Korea.

Few persons, decorators said, inquire about the fiber content when selecting a grasscloth wallpaper. Many would be shocked to know they are enjoying the beauty of kudzu right on their walls.

The grasscloth is usually selected for its interesting texture and the soft, natural sheen. Although it comes in a variety of colors, the best selling colors are those closest to the natural color of the fibers. These range from golden honey to ripe chestnut.

Grasscloth wallpaper is expensive. A double roll, which covers about fifty square feet of wall space, sells in 1996 for about $50.00. Most dealers do not stock it but keep samples from which customers can make their selections and the dealer then orders it from a wholesaler.

We could find no record anywhere of anyone, or any firm, in the United States that has attempted the manufacture of grasscloth wallpaper from kudzu.

Kudzu Clothmaking in Japan

Kudzu is made into a fabric in Japan today, as it has been for thousands of years, by a company called Kawade Kokichi Shoten in the village of Kakegawa. The fabric, which in America we would probably call cloth, is called kudzu-fu. It is woven from the fibers extracted from the kudzu vines and is very durable.

Kawade Kokichi Shoten uses the traditional hand methods to produce kudzu fabric. This makes the labor cost more because there are few skilled workers and the production time is much longer than it would be if machine methods were used. But the kudzu fibers are spun and woven by hand.

Since the interest in folk arts and crafts has become popular again in Japan, many more customers are asking for, and buying, kudzu-fu.

How Kudzu-fu is Produced

Skilled farmers collect the kudzu vine and work in the basic processes of extracting the fiber from them. They do this work during the summer when they are not busy at work in the tea fields for which Kakegawa is also famous.

The fresh vines are boiled for half an hour and then soaked in a steam for half a day. They are then buried in a bed of grass and straw for three days to decompose. After decomposition is complete, the vines are soft and the skin is removed from the vine to expose the strands of fibers which have grown tightly together.

The fiber cores are pulled free of the skin and wrapped in to skeins in the shape of a figure eight. The skeins are then bleached in rice water overnight, washed again, and then dried in the open air in the shade.

After they are dry, the fiber cores are carefully pulled apart. This yields very thin threads which must be tied together to form continuous yarn.

The knots are small but prevent kudzu from being used for the warp, which is silk, cotton or hemp, but the knots give the finished cloth its characteristic uneven pattern. The finished cloth is beaten with a wooden mallet to mesh the fibers and give it a sheen.

Kudzu cloth is not considered feasible for everyday wear but is used in many practical items such as purses, handbags, cushions, decorative wall hangings, cloth for the Japanese Tea Ceremony, spectacle cases and many similar personal care items.

These products are sold in Kakegawa where they are made and in Tokyo, Osaka and other large cities in Japan.

Efforts are underway to develop machinery to process kudzu for cloth. If this occurs, production will increase. If the machinery is developed, there is an abundance of free raw material in the Southeast just waiting to be turned into kudzu cloth.

Or better yet, a citizen of the Southeast may develop the machinery and make lots, of all kinds, of kudzu cloth!

Chapter 24
Kudzu as a Medicine

For Treatment of Alcoholism

Dr. Wing-Ming Keung of Harvard University Medical School said in June 1966 that their basic research on kudzu as a treatment for alcoholism has produced very promising results. The next phase in the research is clinical testing with human patients. This phase will begin as soon as there is money to pay for it.

The basic research on kudzu began in 1990. The objective is to test kudzu to determine if it can be developed into an effective therapeutic medicine with which to treat alcoholism. Two extracts from kudzu, daidain and daidzein, will be tested on human patients. Both of these have suppressed alcohol consumption in Syrian golden hamsters, the test animals. There were no adverse side effects.

Why Test a Kudzu - A Weed?

The decision to test kudzu was based upon its use in the Orient. Chinese physicians and herbal doctors have used kudzu to treat alcoholism for thousands of years. However, it has not been a general practice for them to record their modes of therapy and the results. Despite this, the continued use of kudzu indicated they found it to be an effective treatment. Hence, investigative research of this traditional medicine for a disease so disruptive and destructive in human society appeared to be a sound endeavor. Since documents were not available, personal contact was made.

Dr. Wing-Ming Keung visited seven medical colleges and hospitals and three research institutes in China to collect clinical information on their use of kudzu in the treatment of alcoholism. He interviewed thirteen traditional physicians and research scientists. All of them generally agreed that kudzu extracts are effective in suppressing the appetite for alcohol and its deleterious effects on the vital human organs.

The physicians Dr. Keung interviewed had treated a total of 300 alcohol abusers with kudzu based medications. In all cases, these medications were considered effective in both controlling and suppressing the appetite for alcohol and improving the functions of the alcohol-affected vital organs. Significant improvement was observed with a week of treatment. After 2-4 weeks, about 80% of the patients no longer craved alcohol. Alleviation of some of the alcohol-induced damage to some vital organs usually requires 4-6 months.

No side effects associated with the use of kudzu extracts have ever been reported.

Precisely how the kudzu extract works within the human body to suppress the craving for alcohol has yet to be determined. It has been established that it does work in all laboratory animals tested. It is anticipated that it will work effectively and safely in human patients.

~~~~~~~~~~~~

Self-medication with Kudzu Extracts

Several companies are now selling kudzu extract, citing the fact that it has been shown effective in suppressing a craving for alcohol. Most sales literature, if seen in the full text, contains a disclaimer intended to shield the seller from liability. The extracts are expensive and some of the sales hyperbole touts them as something of a medicinal panacea.
~~~~~~~~~~~~

None of these extracts are approved or endorsed by anyone affiliated with the on-going studies of kudzu at Harvard Medical School.

Any person considering self-medication should be aware that kudzu may interact with other medications present at the same time in the body and produce a different result than if taken as a single medication. This question will be addressed during the clinical testing at Harvard.

Herbal Medicine

Herbal medicine has been a part of every civilization. China and Egypt have the earliest recorded use of herbs. Some authorities claim that an Emperor of China called Huang-ti, who reigned about 2637 B.C. composed a treatise on herbal medicine. Chin-nong, another emperor composed a catalog of Chinese herbs about 2699 B.C. and it is believed kudzu is listed in it.

The earliest verifiable records show that kudzu was in use as an herbal medicine as early as 200 B.C.. It is used as a treatment for intestinal disturbances, consumptive thirst, colds, flu, stiffness and general muscle pain.

The kudzu root is the part of the plant used most often, although some use is made of the leaves. The root is dried or processed into a powder which is described as sweet and acrid in taste. The root is a mild acting substance high in starch. Its properties are believed to neutralize acidity and promote an alkaline condition in the body which leads to the relief of pain.

The origin of this conceptional theory can be traced back to the East. Taoist teachings of yin and yang are based upon the principle that the yin and yang must be in proper balance for a person to have good health. Yin and yang are somewhat analogous to acidic and alkaline as used in the West. When there is too much yin or too much yang, poor health is the consequence.

Kudzu leaves are also used to make teas. They are sometimes dried and are often used in the green state. The kudzu leaves are generally combined with other herbs for medicinal reasons or flavor preferences. Ginger and cinnamon are frequently used. Many persons make and drink tea for the pleasure of it as well as for medicinal reasons.

Herbalists all over the globe believe herbs to be the safest medicines available. They caution, however, that improper use, or the amount used, can cause side effects.

Readers interested in learning more about kudzu as used in herbal medicine, or herbal medicine in general, will find many excellent books on the subject at large bookstores, health food stores or the public library.

Herbalists may be found in the yellow pages of many telephone directories. Herb groups exist in many parts of the country.

As with any new endeavor, check carefully to ascertain facts before plunging.

Part V

What Lies Ahead

Chapter 25
Kudzu Vigil at the Red Barn

Sharon and Scott Theiss of Lake Lure, North Carolina keep a constant vigil daily to prevent kudzu from reclaiming their Red Barn. They wrested it away from kudzu in 1994. As you can see from the photo below, kudzu had a firm grip on it, and had been in sole control since 1974.

The Red Barn in Summer 1994

The Theisses wanted the Red Barn and the three acres around it for a business. An army of workers attacked the kudzu first with machetes, then with Roundup mixed with oil so it would stick to the leaves and vines. Kudzu retreated but did not surrender. Within days after the vines were cut to earth level, and sprayed generously, defiant green shoots would appear. The battle continued until winter arrived and the barn was liberated. Scott Theiss remarked that he had never seen a living thing so well suited to survive! The photograph below shows that, for now, kudzu is at bay.

The Red Barn in Summer1996

The Theisses have established their business in the Red Barn. Kudzu still makes its underground presence known by sending up green at random spots throughout the three acres. So, a constant daily vigil is mandatory to 'discourage' new growth.

Before Kudzu

The town of Lake Lure, North Carolina built the Red Barn in 1948 as a Community Center. For many years, this post and beam "barn" was used for square and round dances, parties, craft shows, antique auctions and Sunday church services.

After the town of Lake Lure renovated the old train depot for a community center, the barn fell into disrepair, as you can see in this photograph.

The Red Barn in the early 1970s, before Kudzu took over

Kudzu swallowed the old red barn. Despite these indignities, it was featured in the mystery novel *Star Flight* by Phyllis Whitney who visited the Lake Lure area and chose it as the setting for this book.

Kudzu in its Proper Place

The barn is now a bright, barn red instead of the kudzu green in summer and kudzu brown in winter. It looks brand new and houses a craft shop and tea room called The Red Barn and Bear Company.

Kudzu is lurking about on the grounds, and on the shelves of the gift shop and tea room. The Red Barn and Bear Company sells all types of kudzu crafts and a large quantity of kudzu jelly. These products come from other locales but if a local kudzu supply is ever needed, all the Theisses need do is stop 'discouraging' the kudzu growth!

KUDZU KLASS

Kudzu potpourri: Regina Hines of Ball Ground, Georgia has developed a Kudzu Potpourri and a Kudzu Potpourri Oil. She combines kudzu flowers, pods, vines and other treasures from the kudzu patch to create a potpourri that has the grapelike fragrance of the kudzu flowers.

Chapter 26
How to Grow Kudzu
By: Harry J. Amling

Harry J. Amling is a Professor Emeritus of Horticulture at Auburn University, Auburn, Alabama. He taught classes in Plant Growth and Development, Plant Physiology, Nutrition of Horticulture Plants, Nut (pecan) Culture, Small Fruit Culture, and Plant Propagation, during his 30 year tenure at Auburn. He currently resides in Opelika, Alabama.

Professor Amling appreciates the ambivalent state of kudzu affairs, which is nothing new. He told us that while trying to develop a procedure for growing kudzu seedlings, there were baby kudzu plants in pots (which incidentally, the deer love) on one side of the building, and at the same time efforts were required to keep wild kudzu from encroaching into the yard on the other side of the building.

He likes to mention that kudzu produces a very fragrant lavender flower in the latter half of the summer, plus providing abundant shade as a vertically-raised vine. He suggests, "Try a kudzu plant in a large tub as a porch plant because you'll like it."

Kudzu likes sun, full sun if possible.

How to Grow Kudzu

There are three ways to propagate kudzu: from seed, from nodes on vines, and from wild plants.

From Seed

Only seedlings produce tap roots, from which starch can be extracted. This tap root appears to be very fleshy and without any apparent root hairs. Consequently, the seedlings cannot stand up to weed competition, particularly grasses which do have root hairs.

Seed pods are collected from vines growing vertically on houses, trees, telephone poles, and other vertical supports, in September. Prostrate vines produce few, if any flowers or hairy seed pods. If you wait until October in central Alabama to do your collecting, the pods will have already fallen off. Just try finding these fallen pods in a kudzu patch!

Pods we collected had 1 to 4 seeds each. The seeds are very small, perhaps 1/16 inch in diameter. They are what we refer to as hard seed. The seed coat needs to be eroded, or broken up, for water to be absorbed to start the germination process. We soaked our seeds in concentrated sulfuric acid for 60 to 90 minutes, then *THOROUGHLY* rinsed them with water. The seeds were then sowed in deep trays, 3 to 4 inches, in commercial seed growing media, at a depth of about 1/4 inch.

At the time the seed emerges and the first leaves are seen, the root will be about 2 inches long already. These should be carefully transplanted into deep pots, and you are on your way to raising a kudzu plant.

From Nodes on Kudzu Vines

Kudzu vines have the potential to form roots at every node where there is a leaf, if the node is covered with soil and kept moist. After roots form, cut that section of the vine out and you have what is referred to as a crown plant. The root system will be a fibrous one, and not a fleshy taprooted one.

From Wild Kudzu Plants

You can find new crown plants in the field; however, digging up established tap-rooted vines in the woods or fields is next to impossible. Most are mixed up with pine or other tree roots. Also, the large tuberous roots go halfway to China! If you find any crown plants, cover with soil and keep the soil moist but not wet.

Kudzu Requirements for Growth

The kudzu plant like good, moisture-holding capacity soil that is below pH7.5. It is not a desert plant. It likes a lot of water, but does not tolerate wet feet or swampy conditions. Silt or clay soil are more suited to vigorous growing kudzu plants than are coarse, sandy soils.

Kudzu vines have survived freezing temperatures -8 degrees Fahrenheit on our farm. However, the roots probably cannot survive deep frozen ground, which limits its growth in the northern range.

Kudzu likes sun, full sun if possible. That is why it grows better around the periphery of a woods than in the center of it.

KUDZU KLASS

Survival with Kudzu? Kudzu roots can be eaten as a vegetable. The root is similar to a potato, except *much* larger, taste sweet and are rich in starch. Wash, peel, cut in small pieces and either steam, boil or fry, or eat raw.

Dr. Robert Tanner, a chemical engineer at Vanderbilt University in Nashville, Tennessee says kudzu has saved the Japanese from famine in times gone by. The Japanese would just go up in the mountains and survive on kudzu!

This led Dr. Tanner to another conclusion. In the event of a nuclear disaster, kudzu may be what saves the people of the South. Kudzu roots grow to great depths in the soil while radiation penetrates one or two inches.

Chapter 27
An Ecologist and Kudzu

Dr. James H. Miller is a Research Ecologist at the United States Department of Agriculture Forest Service at Auburn University in Alabama. He graciously allowed us to print some of his writings about kudzu.

How I Got to Know Kudzu gives us a glimpse of some of the events in Dr. Miller's journey along the road he traveled to become an expert on kudzu.

There is a tendency for non-scientists to view scientific experts as persons not tethered with human emotions, trials and tribulations. Facts are their prey; they manipulate them and produce amazing results. Dr. Miller's story is a refreshing reminder that scientific experts also function in the whirlpool of human existence.

His second article, *Kudzu Eradication and Management* in Chapter 28, gives our readers the best information available in June 1996 on how to deal with kudzu. Dr. Miller included a Recommendation Summary at the conclusion of this comprehensive information which can be used as a convenient reference. Now, enjoy a very sage saga.

How I Got to Know Kudzu
By: Dr. James H. Miller

When I was a much younger forest researcher arriving in the South about 18 years ago, kudzu struck me as a strange plant -- a plant bully -- one that could get it over on the other plants. At least like a giant in a fairy tale it sleeps for a few months each year to give everyone a rest -- plants and people. Even when I was in the tropics of southeast Asia before coming here, I saw no plant with such power to take over land so completely, excluding other plants. I had come to the South as a member of a new U. S. Forest Service research team. Our mission was to study plants that compete with southern pines and hardwoods and learn how to control them using herbicides, burning, and mechanical treatments. It was not long before one person then another would ask me what could control kudzu. Well, it was an interesting question but it was not the most important question being asked me, those came from the older research managers -- my bosses.

For the first summer, I tried to ignore kudzu and just listened to the jokes that everyone seemed to have about the plant. Then that winter I received a letter that would change my life. The letter was from an elderly lady that had a desperate tone. She related that kudzu surrounded her home in the country, and her husband had fought it back until he had passed away a few years before, and now she was unable to keep up the fight. She told of her horrible recurring nightmares of kudzu coming through the windows at night and grabbing her. The sincere plea for help struck me in the heart. I decided we should be able to find the right herbicides and other means to defeat this beast -- even though I was instructed not to work on such a trivial matter.

I Went in Search of Kudzu

So I started to study earlier research and everything I could learn about kudzu. Before long the jokes I heard had lost their humor, because other landowners learned of my interest and told me of their plight. Most had paid applicators to spray their kudzu, again and again, with this and that herbicide that was supposedly guaranteed to kill it. Some had paid thousands of dollars and still had kudzu. They were being flimflammed right and left. Almost every herbicide sold at that time had a claim to kill kudzu, and few knew what really worked.

Well after about five years of wading through knee-deep to chest-high kudzu testing 25 herbicides at many locations, and retreating and retreating and treating members of my crew for heat exhaustion, I was ready to hit the road to speak at county meetings all over Alabama telling folks how to kill it. Then I traveled to other States, as I still do, to tell how to fight kudzu toe-to-toe and *win.* Only three herbicides were found effective and the rest were about no good. The good ones are Tordon, Spike, and Veteran -- actually Tordon is the best. Then I had to contend with the other herbicide companies that now planned to discredit me and my findings so they could continue to sell ineffective herbicides and flimflam people like snake-oil salesmen. They didn't know that I had learned to persevere by wading through kudzu, crawling through kudzu, and chainsawing through some. All I wanted was for folks that have kudzu to have the best information available. Most southern states now have extension publications reporting mine and other's findings on the best herbicides and exact treatment methods that must be followed to be successful.

Coming to Terms with Kudzu

Since that time I have grown mellow. I think kudzu is pretty neat -- a unique landscape characteristic of the South. You're right, I don't have kudzu on my land. What a green, green plant it is. Nice ladies have given me nice-looking kudzu baskets after talks. In fact we have an angel made from kudzu vines on our porch. Exactly, I won't let it in the house and I keep a check for any possible sprouting. I have eaten raw kudzu root in China, in a park on Sunday afternoon. It is a cheap candy over there, sold by the slice. It is like eating raw potatoes but better. It first tastes like starch, but then your mouth turns it into a burst of sugar. Also, my wife has stir-fried some peeled shoots which were salty and had plenty of fiber for my diet. I have taken my family 100's of miles out of the way on vacations to see kudzu patches in Oklahoma. People use to call day and night wanting to know how to control it and some how to grow it. After a while my wife and children could take the calls and give the details.

I have learned that if we are to bring kudzu into harmony with the other plants then we will need to find the insects and microbes that feed on it naturally in its home range in China and see which ones are safest to import into this country. Of course, it will take much money to find those insects that do not feed on any other plants. Then if we are successful, kudzu will be much meeker and will be more easily controlled by other much cheaper means. Yes, there will still be kudzu left in the South for baskets, jelly, etc., but it won't be a bully anymore. It will have learned what being neighborly means in the South. If we don't teach it a lesson then we can expect kudzu to romp and stomp on more land.

Note: I am a U.S. Government employee and all my writings are in the public domain and cannot be copyrighted.

~~~~~~~~~~~~

Authors' Note: The articles written by Dr. James H. Miller which appear in this book are an exception to the restrictions on the copyright page of this book, *Kudzu The Vine to Love or Hate.*
~~~~~~~~~~~~

Chapter 28
Kudzu Eradication and Management

By: Dr. James H. Miller
USDA Forest Service, Southern Research Station
Auburn University, Alabama

Kudzu patches can be eradicated with *persistent* treatments or they can be contained and managed with other treatment options. Herbicides, grazing, prescribed burning, and disk harrowing can be used as eradication or containment treatments. For eradication, every kudzu plant in and around a patch must be killed or the spread from any surviving plants can make all prior efforts and investments useless. This means that all landowners sharing a patch must arrange to treat the whole patch simultaneously.

Landowners often find herbicide applications the easiest means for eradication and containment but herbicides should only be applied according to exact label instructions, requirements, and prohibitions. Read, understand, and follow herbicide labels completely before and during use. Commercial firms that are licensed herbicide applicators can be contracted to perform herbicide applications, but in most cases the landowner must give directions if the treatment is to be successful and cost effective.

Kudzu Containment and Management

Kudzu is difficult to contain because vine runners on the soil surface can grow up to a foot a day in the spring. Newly rooted plantlets then occur at every node on these runners. Kudzu also has rhizomes (underground runners) and these will spread the plants. Containment then requires cutting these runners and herbicide treatments to control newly emerging plants. The ability of kudzu to spread increases as the plants age, because their roots are growing larger with time. Thus, mowing and herbicide applications of the entire patch area are used to weaken kudzu plants to prevent rapid spreading. The less effective herbicides discussed later can be used for this purpose.

Eradication using Livestock Grazing

One treatment option for some landowners is livestock grazing. Close grazing for 3 to 4 years can eliminate kudzu when 80 percent or more of the vegetative growth is continuously consumed. All types of grazing animals will readily eat kudzu, but cattle grazing has shown the most success in eradication.

It is particularly helpful if kudzu is overgrazed in August and September of each year. Then fast growing tree species should be established at close spacing or pasture grasses planted and grazing pressure continued for one or two additional years. Grazing requires fencing around the area that is to be eradicated and a source of water, plus supplemental feed to maintain livestock health. Also, vines must be cut from draped trees within the area so that animals can reach the foliage. Kudzu plants that persist after grazing can be eliminated with spot applications of herbicides.

Eradication using Herbicides

Successful eradication programs using herbicides require that the following jobs be performed correctly: 1} identify and inspect the site from which kudzu is to be eradicated, 2} prepare the site, 3} select the most effective herbicides, 4} treat properly, 5} retreat when necessary, and finally 6} establish desirable vegetation such as trees or grasses for long-term suppression of any emerging kudzu. Standards for what constitutes correct performance of each of these jobs is defined in the following paragraphs.

{1} Site Inspection

Each patch of kudzu should be inspected closely before treatments begin. This inspection, if done properly, will permit a more careful plan of attack on the patch. There are several basic situations that will require different treatment methods. These are:

a} open patches on level ground,
b} patches near ponds, streams, and ditch banks,
c} residential sites,
d} young pine plantations,
e} non-croplands like fence-rows, and
f} forest openings with kudzu in desirable trees.

In the winter or early spring when kudzu is dormant, walk over the patch and determine which situations identified in a} through f} exist in the patch you want to eradicate. Next, identify the boundaries of each situation within the patch.

The location of nearby sensitive crops like soybeans, peanuts, and cotton, or gardens or ornamental trees should also be noted. Streams, gullies, ponds, and ditch banks should be identified and their surrounding slopes estimated as far as possible routes of herbicide movement during rain storms.

Eradication difficulty and herbicide rates will be determined by the age of the patch. Older kudzu patches, with large roots, are the most difficult to eradicate. Roots will be large when the patch is over 10 years old or when vines have spread into nearby trees. Examine the kudzu root crowns, which are woody knots at the soil surface. If many of the root crowns are over 2 inches in diameter, it will probably require a higher herbicide rate and more retreatments for eradication. Higher rates and more treatments will also be required on clayey soils, especially if there are numerous rocks or old terraces, or both. Also, downed trees and debris will hinder herbicides from reaching hidden kudzu plants. Kudzu is especially difficult to eradicate under these situations.

{2} Site Preparation

For some patches, prescribed burning can be used not only to reduce debris for more effective treatment but also to kill small kudzu plants and to sever tree-draped vines. Burning will kill only the very small plants. A good time to burn is in February and early March when dead kudzu leaves are compacted for good fuel and winter exposure to erodible soils can be minimized following the burn.

Many hazards can be found after a burn, such as old wells and gullies. For safety, each hazard should be flagged with a very tall pole. Also, the size and density of kudzu root crowns can be readily seen after a burn. This helps identify the areas within the patch that will require higher rates of herbicide or more coverage.

Logging of kudzu-draped trees is advised one year in advance of treatment, if possible. Winter logging can permit the logs to be skidded into the patch so that vines are not spread further with logging. Skidding outside the patch will invariably spread kudzu.

Both grazing by livestock and disking with a harrow can be used for one or two summers prior to treatment to weaken the kudzu plants. Disking can also be used several months after treatment to help disrupt and dislodge weakened kudzu roots.

{3} Effective Herbicides

Open Patches on Level Ground

Most herbicides will brown kudzu leaves and vines, but few will result in root control. Tordon 101 Mixture and Tordon K (see the Recommendation Summary at the end of this Chapter for the common names and manufacturers) are the most cost-effective herbicides of the 25 tested on kudzu over an 8-year period. Both herbicides are applied as sprays to the foliage and then must be washed from the leaves by rainfall to the roots for uptake. Both of these are **restricted use herbicides** because they are very water soluble and can leach through sandy soils into streams and ground water, nearby trees with roots in the area can be killed or injured. Many crops are very sensitive to these herbicides, and they are relatively persistent and may injure or kill plants introduced into the area too soon. Because of this a permit for purchase is issued by your county agent or state regulatory agency after proper use procedures are reviewed. Kudzu is a legume and Tordon herbicides are very effective on leguminous plants.

Effective rates are:

Kudzu less than 10 years old

a. Tordon 101 Mixture at 1 gallon per acre
b. Tordon K at 0.5 gallons per acre
c. Tordon 101 Mixture at 0.5 gallon per acre
+ Tordon K at 1 quart per acre

Kudzu more than 10 years old

a. Tordon 101 Mixture at 2 gallons per acre
b. Tordon K at 1 gallon per acre
c. Tordon 101 Mixture at 1 gallon per acre
+ Tordon K at 0.5 gallon per acre

The higher rates should be used on patches that are

older than 10 years and on clayey and stony soils. Application of these herbicides can occur from June through September (see later section on application). Treatments should not be made with Tordon until at least June, because all kudzu plants must be growing at the time of treatment for control to be effective. Kudzu plants do not all emerge in a patch at the same time.

Rainfall is required within 2 - 5 days after application for good control to occur with Tordon herbicides. Ideally, rainfall less than one inch should occur 2 to 3 days after application. The herbicide must be washed into the upper soil layer for root uptake after foliar uptake. Also, Tordon is decomposed by sunlight and the longer it remains on the foliage without rainfall the less active ingredient is present. Any trees with roots in or near the treated area may be injured or killed. Even after using the most-effective Tordon herbicides, broadcast retreatments will be required in most cases and spot treatments in all cases, with specifics discussed in later sections.

There are other herbicides that are less effective than Tordon that can be used for containment and management on forested sites, as well as, multi-year treatments for possible eradication. These herbicides are (in decreasing order of effectiveness):

Veteran 720 (formerly Banvel 720) by Riverdale (recom mended at 2 gallons per acre),
Transline by DowElanco (21 ounces per acre),
Krenite by DuPont (3 gallons per acre),
Garlon 4 and 3A by DowElanco (1 to 2 gallons per acre),
Accord by Monsanto (1 gallon per acre),
Arsenal Applicators Concentrate by American Cyanamid (2 quarts per acre),
Oust by DuPont plus **Accord** (3 ounces plus 2 quarts per acre), and
Escort by DuPont (4 ounces per acre).

These herbicides work best on patches less than 10 years

old, but may require two to ten annual broadcast treatments before spot treatments begin. All of these should be applied after midsummer, after draped kudzu has started to flower. Foliar browning will occur with all these herbicides, but re-growth can be expected.

Tordon should not be used near streams, ponds, and other sensitive areas. This chemical can move in rain water, so do not use it where the slope will permit washing into off-site areas or to roots of desirable trees and plants.

Sites near Streams, Ponds, and Ditch Banks

These sites are particularly sensitive because of their proximity to water. Veteran 720, sold by Riverdale Chemical Company, is the herbicide of choice in these situations. This herbicide should not be sprayed directly into water or on ditch banks where runoff will contaminate surface water.

Veteran 720 is applied at 2 gallons per acre for patches less than 10 years old, and at 3 gallons per acre for older patches. Applications should be made in August or September. Veteran 720 should never be applied within or near the root zone of any desirable plant. Moderate rainfall is required for its necessary soil-activation.

Residential Sites

Multiple applications per year can be made with Roundup, sold by Monsanto Chemical Company. Apply Roundup at the rate of 1 to 2 gallons per acre (spot treatment with 2.5 ounces Roundup per gallon of water). Extreme care should be used when spraying around desirable plants so that unseen spray does not drift. Trees with roots in the treated area should not be damaged because Roundup is not soil active. In some cases, continued mowing of invading vines is as effective as making a herbicide application.

Young Pine Plantations

Kudzu invading pine plantations can best be treated with mixtures of Escort (DuPont Chemical Company) with Arsenal AC (American Cyanamid Company) or Accord

(Monsanto Chemical Company). Only partial control can be expected by these treatments when the kudzu has been present for several years.

For treating plantations of 2 year old loblolly pines, apply Escort at 1 to 1.5 ounces per acre with either Arsenal AC at 1 pint or Accord at 1 quart. Apply a single treatment during midsummer when kudzu is actively growing and the pines are not water stressed. Direct the spray away from the young pines when possible, especially the growing tips. Some growth suppression and possible damage of the pine may occur. Two years of treatment will probably be required. If old established kudzu plants are present, they should be spot treated just around the root crown with Tordon. For old kudzu growing in young pines, treatment with Tordon should be considered for eradication, although the pines will be killed.

Non-croplands

Spike herbicides, sold by DowElanco, can be used to eradicate kudzu, often with a single application. Spike 80W, a dry flowable formulation, and Spike 20P pellets are labeled for non-crop areas such as rights-of-ways and fence rows. Effective rates for Spike 80W have been found to be 6 to 8 pounds per acre and for Spike 20P, 20 to 30 pounds per acre. These herbicides can be applied any time of the year, but early spring is best. The long persistence of these soil-active herbicides can provide control for over 3 years.

Caution: Desirable trees and shrubs having roots extending into or near areas treated with Spike will be killed. Spike can move with runoff water and should not be applied to sloped areas where the herbicide will move off-site into sensitive areas. Spike herbicides are very persistent and it may be several years before desirable plants can be planted after treatment.

Forest Openings and Kudzu in Desirable Trees

Apply Transline, sold by DowElanco, at 21 ounces per

acre as a spray solution. This herbicide is safe on many tree species except black locust, redbud, and mimosa. These trees belong to the family of legumes, like kudzu, and Transline is selective for controlling legumes.

{4} Application for Eradication

Complete and thorough coverage by spray mixtures is required by any application approach. Open patches have been successfully treated using sprayers on crawler, skidder, and farm tractors, using truck-mounted spray units and dragging hose; and by backpack sprayers and mistblowers. Helicopter applications are also effective. Large tractor sprayer are useful for breaking through draped kudzu when treating mature patches. The benefits of using tractor sprayers increases as the depth of kudzu increases. Hose and backpack applications become much more difficult and slow when kudzu is over 2 feet deep.

How much spray mixture is needed per acre when treating with Tordon? Many applicators give different answers. Volumes of 40 to 200 gallons per acre are used by some tractor and hose applicators. Obviously there are benefits in coverage by high volumes and possible soil activation can occur with very high volumes. However, the current recommendation is 40 to 80 gallons of spray mixture per acre, because successful eradication has been achieved using these volumes.

Double coverage with a tractor sprayer is one of the best methods for "open-patch" kudzu treatment, where terrain permits. Half the mixture is applied by parallel passes in one direction, and the remaining half is applied using parallel passes that are at right angles to the first. Swath overlaps of 3 to 5 feet are used to further minimize skips that are common with kudzu treatments. Always treat skipped spots soon after browning makes them evident.

Where it is impossible to make right-angled passes,

double coverage can be achieved by retreating a swath in the opposite direction or by using 50-percent swath overlaps. Only by using double coverage, or perhaps high volume coverage with hose applications, is it possible to hold down the number of retreatments. Both options can lower eradication costs and produce quicker results. One broadcast retreatment can usually be eliminated by using double coverage.

Old terraces, common in Piedmont kudzu patches, make tractor spraying difficult. Good control is hard to achieve in terraces, especially in stony soils. It is best to spray along the lower side, into the terrace, applying in both directions, resulting in a slightly higher rate.

Before beginning open-patch treatments with tractor sprayers, make one or more passes around the outer edge of a patch. Boomless spray nozzles can be tilted up on these outer passes to treat up into the draped vines eliminating the need for cutting. A spray gun can also be used to treat vines in trees. Most pines and hardwoods that are larger than 10 inches in trunk diameter will not be killed by spraying the vines with Tordon 101, unless the trees are already weak. Spray guns are also necessary to treat kudzu in gullies and canyons, and steep patches from roadsides.

{5} Retreatment

An applicator or landowner must be persistent in examining patches for up to 10 years after treatment. Most control is accomplished with one or two broadcast treatments, but plants may continue to appear for many years. Of course, patches less than 10 years old will probably be mostly controlled by only one broadcast application of Tordon herbicides. Success with Tordon herbicides is evident by complete browning of the patch within a few weeks after the initial application.

Following a successful initial treatment, retreatments

should then be delayed for 2 years, with a 1 year layout. Broadcast retreatments are usually made using half the rate of the first. In other words, if a successful application is made in year 1, then another broadcast treatment using half the rate should be applied in year 3.

Research has shown that many of the large kudzu roots that are severely injured will not sprout for 2 years, and thus the recommended delay. On older patches, some kudzu will regrow in the year after application, but all injured large rooted plants will lay dormant for 2 or more years before sending up a vine. Retreatments in successive years are needed if Tordon herbicides and double coverage are not used, and if rainfall does not occur within a week after treatment with Tordon.

For spot treating of scattered plants, use the backpack sprayer mixture of 1 pint Tordon 101, 1/2 pint Tordon K, or 1 pint Veteran 720 in 4 to 5 gallons of water. Only the vines near the root crown should be sprayed to medium wetness with this mixture as well as the soil within 1 foot of the root crown (all vines do not have to be treated). When the vines and root-crown area are sprayed to medium wetness, 99-percent effective control can be obtained with these mixtures.

(6) Plant Desirable Trees or Plants

To complete kudzu eradication, establish desirable plants on the area to prevent soil loss and regain productivity. Kudzu should be positively eradicated before planting desirable trees. For older patches, this means a minimum 4 year treatment period using Tordon herbicides: initial broadcast application in year 1, layout in year 2, rebroadcast treatment in year 3, and spot treatments in year 4. Pines and hardwood trees can be planted 6 months after the last treatment with Tordon or Veteran. Further planting delays may be required when multiple year applications have been used on sandy soils.

The timely planting of grass in the fall after treatment can produce severe competition and help control weakened kudzu plants. Many grasses are not injured by residual Tordon and Spike. In fact, these two herbicides are labeled for use on rangeland and pastures. A grass cover helps control kudzu, protects the soil, and replaces the abundant weed growth that follows kudzu eradication.

Recommendation Summary

Persistence is the key to successful kudzu eradication and management.

The most cost-effective treatment for kudzu eradication is Tordon 101 Mixture applied at 2 gallons per acre, or Tordon K applied at 1 gallon per acre, using perpendicular spray passes.

Retreatment after a successful initial treatment should be applied 2 full years after the first. Then spot treatments of remaining plants in the 4th year.

Veteran 720 is a herbicide that can be used near streams and drainage ditches and can provide better than 95-percent control with two broadcast treatments in successive years. Other labeled herbicides are usually less effective than these and can be used for containment and management of kudzu cover.

Spike herbicides show considerable promise for eradication, using a single treatment. Spike herbicides are labeled for non-cropland situations. The long persistence of the soil-active ingredient in Spike continued to provide control over a 3 year period.

Roundup is the safest herbicide of choice for kudzu problems in residential, home-grounds, and other environmentally sensitive sites. Many years of application with Roundup will be required for eradication of older patches. Persistence in the control treatments outlined in this chapter have been successful in eradicating many kudzu patches, and can work for you.

Herbicides registered by the U. S. Environmental Protection Agency for kudzu control

Trade Name	Common Name	Manufacturer
Accord	glyphosate	Monsanto
Arsenal AC	imazapyr	American Cyanamid
Oust	sulfometurn	DuPont
Escort	metsulfuron	DuPont
Krenite	fosamine	DuPont
Garlon 3A	triclopyr	DowElanco
Garlon 4	triclopyr	DowElanco
Roundup	glyphosate	Monsanto
Tordon 101	picloram + 2, 4-D	DowElanco
Tordon K	picloram	DowElanco
Transline	clopyralid	DowElanco
Veteran 720	dicamba + 2, 4-D	Riverdale

CAUTION

Herbicides and pesticides can be injurious to humans, domestic animals, desirable plants, and fish or other wildlife -- if they are not handled properly.

Use all herbicides and pesticides selectively and carefully. Follow recommended practices for the disposal of surplus herbicides and pesticides and their containers.

KUDZU KLASS

Employment: Thousands of persons spend a better part of their lives clearing kudzu from roadsides, railroads, telephone poles, electric poles, ditches, vacant lots, from around homes, in National Forests and Parks, city, county and private parks, farmland and places you will learn about.

Chapter 29
Kudzu Impacts on Ecosystems

Kudzu is disrupting ecosystems in states below Zone 5 of the United States Department of Agriculture Hardiness Zone Map, insidiously and irrevocably, because no one has found a way to control it. The area covered is roughly from Kentucky south and west to Texas.

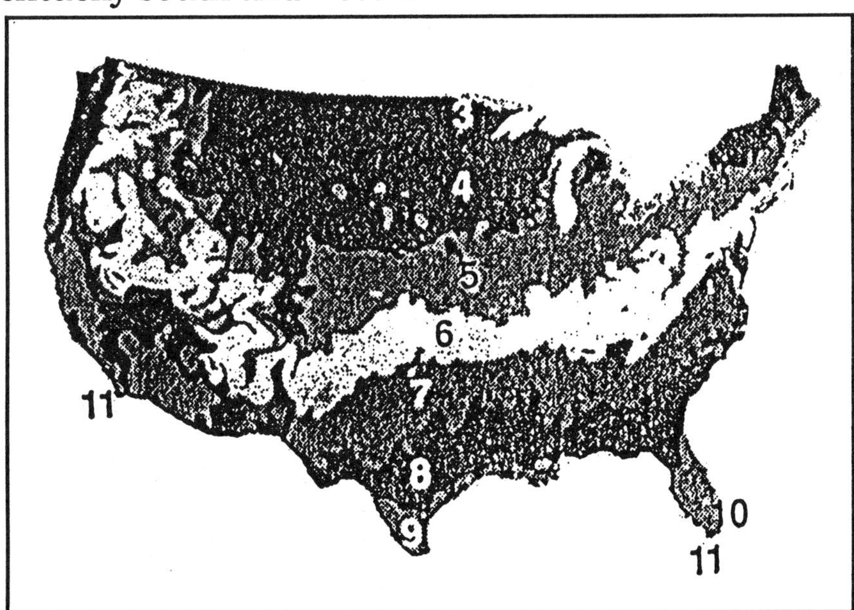

Sustained belcw freezing temperature over a period of days will normally kill kudzu. It appears ice forms in the roots and splinters them beyond healing.

Extinction and replacement is a natural phenomenon in all ecosystems. Kudzu is not an evolutionary replacement for any plant but is here because of deliberate human action for specific ornamental and agricultural purposes. Human food and medicinal uses were not envisioned when kudzu was imported and planted in the United States.

Purposes and Results

Purpose: an ornamental for shade and beauty
Result: satisfactory if kept under tight control

Purpose: erosion control
Result: excellent, except it prevents the development of a native community of plants and covers areas that do not need it for erosion control

Purpose: hay
Result: produces high quality hay but the long vines make it difficult to mow, bale and keep confined to the designated crop area

Purpose: grazing crop
Result: produces abundant foliage, even during severe drought, is well liked by cattle, goats, hogs and chickens; overgrazing has been known to kill it and undergrazing results in it bolting out of control

Purpose: soil improvement
Result: effective because it adds nitrogen to the soil but creates an impenetrably jungle without human intervention

Kudzu provided a satisfactory result for each purpose but with the very unsatisfactory side effect of spreading. In the first part of the twentieth century, spreading was considered a short term problem. Where it was under cultivation, spreading was attributed to inadequate attention or neglect. It was well known that competition is conspicuous, both among plants of the same species and among species with similar needs. Consequently, there was a school of thought that in the long term native plants would rise to the occasion and put kudzu in its place. To date no plants have been equal to the task.

The opinion that kudzu could become a problem and a pest was dismissed by Federal and State agricultural officials so planting was encouraged until it was too late.

Ecology was in its infancy during the time kudzu was considered a magic potion. Ernst Haeckel, a German biologist, introduced the term 'oecology' in 1869. Most American investigations into the interrelations of organisms and their environment were quests for evidence to support the Darwinian theory of natural selection, not find solutions for problems as mundane as a fast growing vine.

The Debate is Over

While humans debated whether kudzu was or would become a problem, it covered over 7,000,000 acres of land in the Southeast. Unless a way is found to stop it, this figure will double in ten years.

The debate is over. Kudzu is changing ecosystems as small as freshwater ponds, a homestead, roadside, or huge slices of a county or state. Even those who recognize and promote the usefulness of kudzu agree.

As we said in the beginning of this book, the purpose is to rouse and share interest in kudzu and suggest its scope rather than attempt to exhaust it. If any reader takes action to control this insistent weed, begins using it, or creates a high volume use for it, our purpose will have been achieved.

Appendix A
Kudzu Information Sources

Arts and Crafts

All of the persons listed in this section do programs in their fields, and may be contacted at the addresses shown here. Those with an * beside the name do art shows also.

Nancy Basket *
Kudzu Kabin Designs
412 Lakeview Heights
Union, SC 29379
(864) 429-3605

Ruth Duncan
Kudzu Kountry
411 Gravel Hill Road
Greenville, AL 36037
(334) 382-8654

Regina Hines *
Kudzu Kreatives
428 Allison Lane
Ball Ground, GA 30107
(770) 479-1262

Diane Hoots *
Krazy Kudzu Products, LTD.
P.O. Box 8584
Warner Robins, GA 31095-8584
Telephone and FAX: (912) 922-6300

Rajeania Snider
426 Russell Road
Rockford, TN 37853
Artist working in Book Arts and Handmade Paper
Mail inquiries only please

Carol Stangler
425 Euclid Terrace, NE
Atlanta, GA 30307
Telephone: (404) 223-0786

Kudzu Activities

Birmingham, Alabama
Kudzu Run in August each year for charity
Sponsored by the *Birmingham Post-Herald* and Sloss Furnaces National Historial Landmark
(205) 324-1911
Features: Run, car show, kudzu arts and crafts, band dance, childrens' activities

Providence Canyon State Conservation Park
Kudzu Takeover Day, held each August since 1985
Features: kudzu activities, arts, crafts, entertainment
Route 1, Box 158
Lumpkin, Georgia 31815
(912) 838-6202

Holly Springs, Mississippi
Kudzu Festival, sponsored by the Chamber of Commerce, 154 South Memphis
(601) 252-2943

Kudzu Education

Anniston Museum of Natural History
4301 McClellan Boulevard
Anniston, Alabama 36202
(205) 237-6767
Since the early 1980s, this museum has held annual classes on kudzu wreath and basket making. They feature films, kudzu food and lectures.

Callaway Gardens
Pine Mountain, Georgia
1-800-282-8181
Frequent display of Discovery Table "Kudzu: The Vine that Ate the South" - showing many kudzu products and photographs.

Schiele Museum
Gastonia, NC
(704) 866-6900
Frequent kudzu workshops and displays. Workshops include making paper, rope, cloth, baskets and jelly.

Teaching Unit: Dorothy Schuyler, a Teacher Consultant,with the Georgia Geographic Alliance and Middle School has developed a teaching unit based on kudzu. This unit is particularly suited to the study of Georgia. The unit includes map and social studies skills, Georgia History, Math, Science, Art, Language Arts and even a guessing game based cn "Kudzu Fact and Fiction." Activities are targeted for the Middle School, but can easily be adapted for other grades. For the cost of printing and shipping, copies of the unit can be obtained by contacting: Dorothy Schuyler, 203 Washingon Way
LaGrange, GA 30240
Telephone: (706) 884-8776

Max Shores at the University of Alabama Center for Public Television and Radio completed a video in April 1996: *The Amazing Story of Kudzu.* For information, call 1-800-463-8825 or check it out on the World Wide Web at http://www.sa.ua.edu.cptr/

Kudzu Farmers

Edith and W. Henry Edwards
Kudzu Konnection
Route 1, Box 718
Rutherfordton, NC 28139
(704) 245-9752

Music

Cassette Tape: The group, Irons in the Fire, has recorded *When the Frost Kills the Kudzu on a cassette* with five other songs. It is sold by Tiger's on the Square, P.O. Box 304, Hayesville, NC, Telephone: (704) 389-6531.

Kudzu Foods

Jelly

Krazy Kudzu Products, LTD.
P. O. Box 8584
Warner Robins, Georgia 31095-8584
Telephone and fax: (912) 922-6300

Thomas Gourmet Foods
P. O. Box 8822
Greensboro, North Carolina 27419
(910) 299-6263

Root Starch

East Earth Trade Winds - direct retail orders
(916) 223-2346

Eden Foods - supplier to health food stores
1-800-248-0301

Harvest Time Natural Foods - direct retail orders
1-800-628-8736

Tree of Life - supplier to health food stores
1-800-223-2910

Appendix B
Kudzu Data Base

The authors of this book have a comprehensive data base on kudzu. If you have kudzu information, pictures, an experience, or story you would like to share, please send it to: Kudzu Data Base, Attention: Juanitta Baldwin, P.O. Box 504, Kodak, TN 37764. We would like to hear from you.

Please send only items you are giving us permission to use at our discretion and you do not wish to have returned. Please do not send items you wish to sell because no items can be returned.

Goodbye
for
now . . .